# Mr Bill
## and the
# Flying Fish

*FOR MY MOTHER*

MR BILL AND THE FLYING FISH: A PICTURE CORGI BOOK 0 552 524417

Originally published in Great Britain in 1985 by Blackie and Son Ltd.

PRINTING HISTORY
Picture Corgi edition published 1987

Text copyright © 1985 Georgie Adams
Illustrations copyright © 1985 Margaret Chamberlain

Picture Corgi Books are published by Transworld Publishers Ltd.,
61-63 Uxbridge Road, Ealing, London W5 5SA, in Australia by Transworld Publishers
(Australia) Pty. Ltd., 15-23 Helles Avenue, Moorebank, NSW 2170, and in New Zealand
by Transworld Publishers (N.Z.) Ltd., Cnr. Moselle and Waipareira Avenues, Henderson,
Auckland.

Made and printed in Portugal by Printer Portugesa.

# Mr Bill
## and the
# Flying Fish

Georgie Adams

*Pictures by* Margaret Chamberlain

PICTURE CORGI BOOKS

Mr and Mrs Bill have a bright, new flower shop on the
corner of Magnolia Mansions. It's halfway down the High
Street in the middle of the town.
In summer, Mrs Bill grows bunches and bunches of
flowers for the shop in her higgeldy-piggeldy garden.
Mrs Bill is a very good gardener.
She has green fingers!

In winter, Mr Bill grows
pots and pots of exotic plants in his greenhouse.
It is hot and steamy in there.
"It's like a blooming jungle," teases Ben.
"Grrr!" growls Micky Mutton, pretending to be a tiger.
"Be off the pair of you!" laughs Mr Bill.

One afternoon, just as Mr Bill was closing the shop, there
came a loud knocking at the door.
Rap, rap.
Tap, tap.
Bang, bang!

Mr Bill opened the door and found his brother, Tom,
standing on the pavement.
Tom was the captain of a deep-sea fishing boat.
"Ahoy there!" he cried. "I've come to pay you a visit."

Mr Bill took Tom home to Pork Pie Cottage.
Young Ben went wild with excitement.
So did Kitty Mitty.

Tom was carrying a large basket that most definitely
smelled of . . . fish.
"Poo what a pong!" laughed Ben.
"Do come in," said Mrs Bill, discreetly holding her nose.

Tom sat down and opened the basket.
"I've got a surprise for you, Ben," he said mysteriously.
"A present from the Indian Ocean."
Ben peered into the basket. There was a fish tank inside
with some strange-looking fish in it.

"What are they?" asked Ben.
"Flying fish," said Tom proudly.
"What nonsense!" laughed Mrs Bill.
"You wait and see," said Tom.

Ben took the fish up to the bathroom and filled the bath
with water.
The fish looked very pleased.
They swam three times round their tank and took a leap
into the bath.

A *flying* leap!
Sploosh,
splosh,
splash!

But next morning, when Mrs Bill went to the bathroom to
wash, she got the most surprising surprise...

The bathroom was full of fish!
"Now, there's a fine thing!" said Mrs Bill crossly, flipping a
fish off her slipper. "The sooner you all go back to the
Indian Ocean, the better!"

Then Ben, Tom and Mr Bill came to see what was the matter.
"Oh dear!" said Ben. "Those fish have multiplied."

The fish were having a whale of a time.
Two were playing leap frog over the soap dish.
One had turned on the cold tap and was sliding
down the waterfall.
And at least a dozen were splashing each other
under the shower.
There was water everywhere!

But there was worse to come.
Kitty Mitty put her head round the door.
Eyes bright,
ears flat,
tail twitching . . .
"Meeeow!" she cried and pounced on the nearest fish.

Well, those poor fish got such a fright, they all flew out of the window!

Ben rushed downstairs and fetched his fishing net. Then he ran down the High Street to see if he could catch them.

Mr and Mrs Bill and Tom were close behind.
They were still in their pyjamas!
"Hello, hello, hello," said a policeman. "What's
all this, then?"

"We are trying to catch some fish," explained Mr Bill.
"A likely story," scoffed the policeman.
Then a flying fish slid down a drainpipe and landed
on his helmet.
"Help!" cried the policeman. "Call the Fire Brigade."

The Fire Brigade came rushing down the High Street
clang,
clang,
clang!

The firemen ran up and down their ladders and turned on
all the hoses but they couldn't catch those fish.

Ben was rushing hither and thither trying to catch them
but it was no use.

There were fish in the fountains, flapping their flippers,
fish in the playpark, paddling in puddles.
Fish in the bathtubs, boating in buckets,
diving off dustbins and down into ditches
until . . .

Tom remembered something an old sailor had
told him once.
And he began to sing.
"Oh, yo ho ho,
And a tiddle um tum,
I'll sail to sea,
In a barrel of rum!"

Tom walked down the High Street singing his song and, as if by magic, the fish came flying after him.
It was the funniest sight you ever saw.
Mr and Mrs Bill, Ben and the policeman, the Fire Brigade and Kitty Mitty, all followed on behind the strange procession.

Soon, they were well out of town and heading
towards a river.
When they got to the river, Tom stopped singing and
pointed to a small rowing boat.

"That's my boat," said Tom. "This river goes all the way to the sea."

Then Tom got into the boat and started singing again.
The flying fish dived in and out of the water and bobbed
up and down in time to Tom's song.
"You'll have to sing all the way back to the Indian Ocean,"
laughed Mr Bill.

"Goodbye!" called Tom.
"Goodbye!" cried Mr and Mrs Bill, the policeman and the
  Fire Brigade.
"Come again soon," called Ben.

Suddenly, Mrs Bill looked down at her feet.
"Mercy me!" she cried.
"What's the matter, Mum?" asked Ben.
"I've still got my slippers on!" she said.

# Collins

## Easy Learning

# Size and measurement

My name is ...................................................................................................

I am ..................... years old.

## Carol Cornwell

# How to use this book

- Find a quiet, comfortable place to work, away from other distractions.

- This book has been written in a logical order, so start at the first page and work your way through.

- Help with reading the instructions where necessary, and ensure that your child understands what to do.

- This book is a gentle introduction to size and measurement. Use plenty of practical examples to make these concepts real. Try to use the following language as you work through the book together: big, bigger, biggest, small, thick, thin, tall, long, short, late, early, more than, less than, first, last, full, empty, half, medium, large, same and different.

- If an activity is too difficult for your child then do more of our suggested practical activities (see Activity note) and return to the page when you know that they're likely to achieve it.

- Always end each activity before your child gets tired so that they will be eager to return next time.

- Help and encourage your child to check their own answers as they complete each activity.

- Let your child return to their favourite pages once they have been completed. Talk about the activities they enjoyed and what they have learnt.

## Special features of this book:

- **Activity note:** situated at the bottom of every left-hand page, this suggests further activities and encourages discussion about what your child has learnt.

- **Size and measurement panel:** situated at the bottom of every right-hand page, this is designed to summarise what has been learnt. It shows the sizes and measurements that have been covered, and highlights the sizes and measurements being learnt on the page.

- **Labelled pictures:** situated on every left-hand page (until page 16), these should be used to introduce the size or measurement concept. Spend time using the pictures to discuss big and small, for example.

- **Certificate:** the certificate on page 24 should be used to reward your child for their effort and achievement. Remember to give them plenty of praise and encouragement, regardless of how they do.

Published by Collins
An imprint of HarperCollinsPublishers
77–85 Fulham Palace Road
Hammersmith
London
W6 8JB

Browse the complete Collins catalogue at
www.collins.co.uk

First published in 2006
© HarperCollinsPublishers Limited 2008

10 9

ISBN-13 978-0-00-730093-8

The author asserts the moral right to be identified as the author of this work.

British Library Cataloguing in Publication Data

A Catalogue record for this publication is available from the British Library.

Written by Carol Cornwell
Design and layout by Lodestone Publishing Limited, Uckfield, East Sussex; www.lodestonepublishing.com
Illustrated by Jenny Tulip
Cover design by Susi Martin
Cover illustration by John Haslam
Printed and bound in China

# Contents

# Big and small

big

small

● Colour the bigger cake.

Look at different sized objects together and use the suggested mathematical language to make comparisons. Ask: 'Which is the biggest? Which is the smallest?'

● Draw a smaller house.

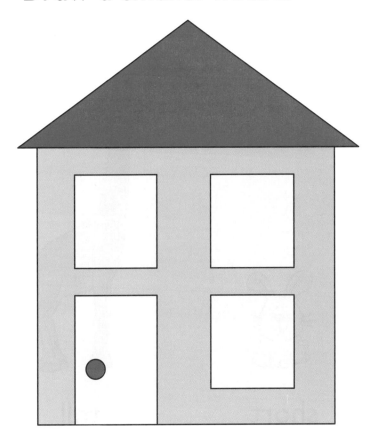

● Draw a yellow circle round the biggest animal.
Draw a green circle round the smallest animal.

# Long, short and tall

long          short          tall

● Draw longer whiskers on cat ② .

Measure the height of your child and other members of the family. Make a chart to show all of the sizes. Use the chart to ask: 'Who is the tallest? Who is the shortest?' Amend the chart as your child grows and review the changes together.

- Which scarf is shorter? (✔)

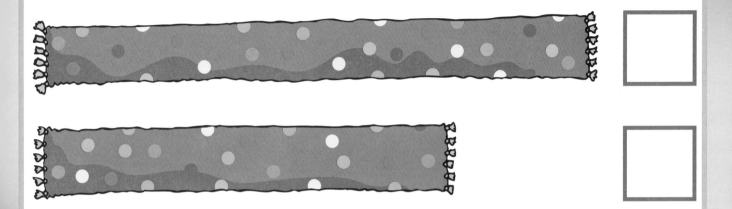

- Draw a pink circle round the tallest animal.
  Draw a purple circle round the longest animal.
  Draw a brown circle round the shortest animal.

# High and low

high                      low

● Colour the higher hot-air balloon red.

Help your child to find objects that are up high in the room, such as the ceiling, lights, items at the top of a bookcase, etc. Repeat the activity for items that are down low. Try playing the same game when you're outside. What can you see up high in the sky? A bird, hot-air balloon, plane, etc.

- Which toy is lower? (✔)

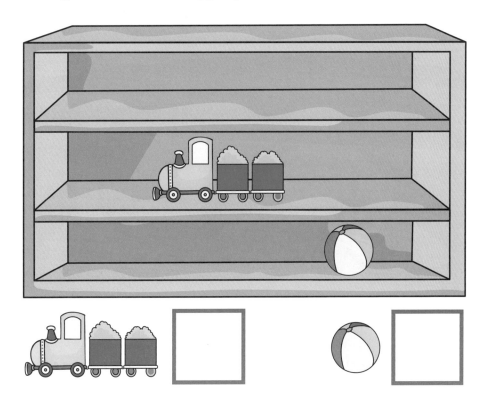

- Draw a pink ⬭circle⬭ round the highest bird.

  Draw a black ⬭circle⬭ round the lowest butterfly.

# Wide and narrow

wide                    narrow

● Which mouse hole is wider? (✔)

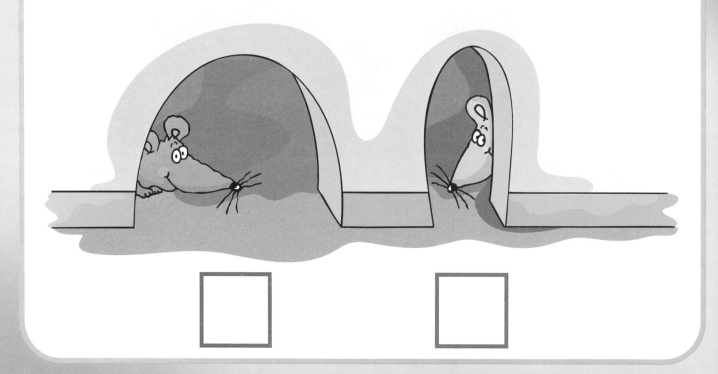

Encourage your child to identify wide and narrow objects and to use this vocabulary to compare the sizes of buildings, doors and windows, etc.

- Colour the narrower tree.

- Colour the narrowest window yellow.
  Colour the widest window orange.

# Thick and thin

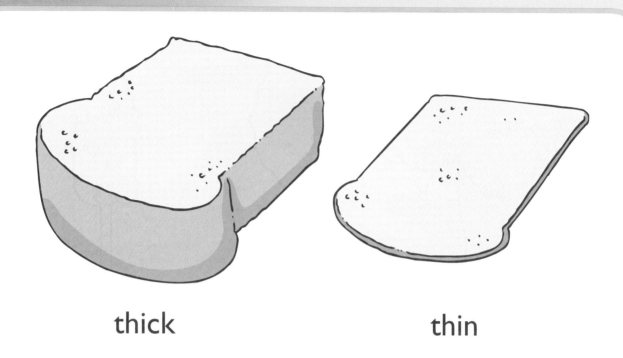

thick                    thin

● Which sandwich is thicker?  (✔)

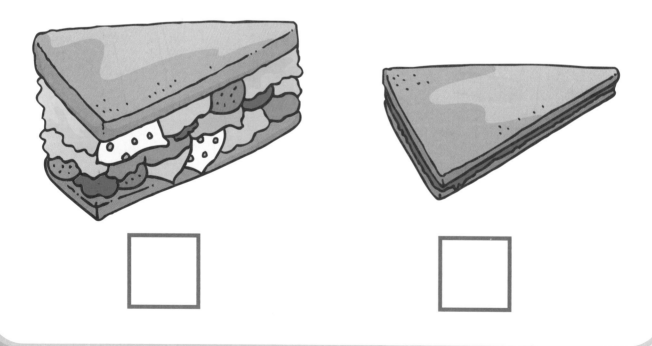

Talk about the thickness of bread when you're making sandwiches together. Try and find
fillings to go in the sandwich that are thin, such as slices of cheese and tomato, etc.

● Draw a (circle) round the boy wearing the thinner jumper.

● Colour the thinnest book blue.
Colour the thickest book red.

# Heavy and light

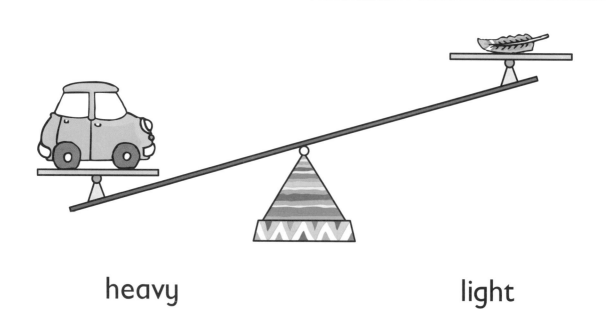

heavy                  light

● Who is heavier? (✔)

Cooking activities are invaluable for measuring and weighing. Show your child how to read scales and see when things are heavy or light.

## Which animal is lighter? Draw a ⟨circle⟩ round it.

## Colour the heaviest present purple.
## Colour the lightest present green.

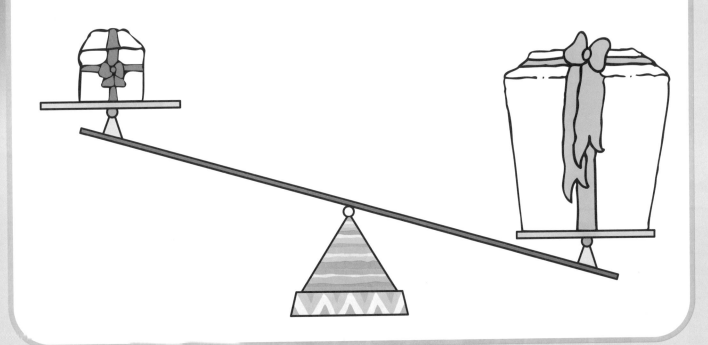

# Small, medium and large

● Draw a line to join the three bears to their correct chair and bed.

small          medium          large

It is important for your child to notice and identify differences in size and to be able to grade them. Compare items at home such as shoes, clothes and beds, etc.

# Far and near

- Draw a balloon near the tree.

- Draw a tree far from the house.

# More and less

● Draw a circle round the jar that has more sweets.

● Who has less dinner?  (✔)

# Full and empty

- Which bag is full? (✔)

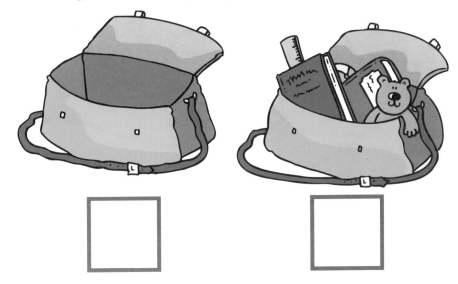

□ □

- Draw a circle round the empty glass.

- Colour the bath so it is half full.

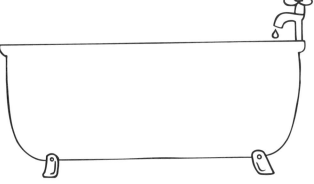

# First and last

● Which boy will get home first?

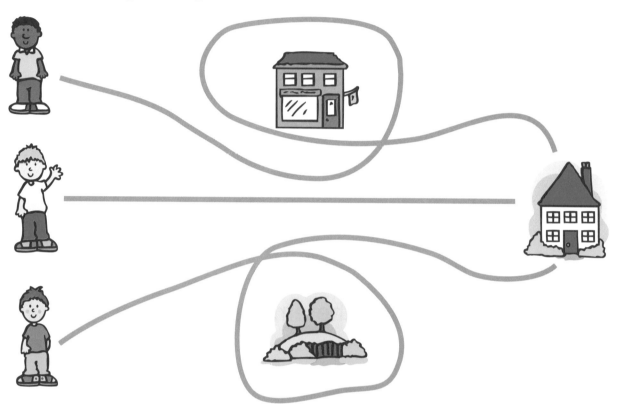

● Who will come last in the race? Write the number.

Talk about different speeds with your child. Try having a fun race to see who can win a running race or finish a jigsaw first. Say: 'You finished your jigsaw first, I was last.' Sand timers are good fun too, and great to race against when tidying up!

# Same and different

- Look at the pictures in each row. Draw a (circle) round the one that is different.

- Make picture 2 the same as picture 1.

1   2

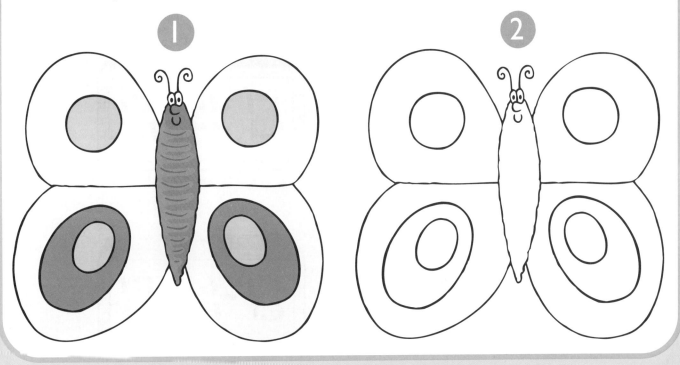

# Time

- Colour the sky blue or black to show if it is daytime or night.

- Draw lines to join the clocks that show the same time.

Time is often a difficult concept to understand. You can make it easier by making a visual timetable with pictures. Draw a relevant picture for each day of the week; for example if your child goes swimming on Mondays then draw, or use a photograph, of them swimming. Stick them on a piece of string and hang the timetable up. Move a paperclip along to mark where you are in the week.

Look at the pictures. Draw hands on the clocks to show the time that you do these things.

What time is it? Write the number.

 o'clock      □ o'clock      □ o'clock

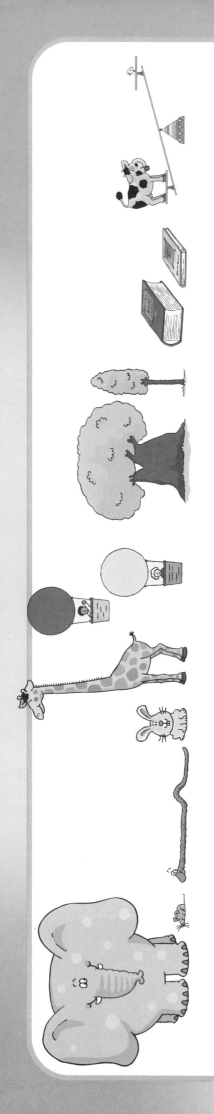

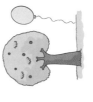
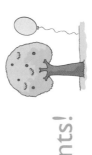

Well done .................................... (name)

You have finished!

Now you know all your sizes and measurements!

Date .........................................

Age .........................................

# GCSE Success

## Chemistry

**Dan Evans**

Exam Practice Workbook

# Chemistry

## Atomic Structure and the Periodic Table

## Structure, Bonding and the Properties of Matter

## Quantitative Chemistry

## Chemical and Energy Changes

Contents

## The Rate and Extent of Chemical Reactions

## Organic Chemistry

## Chemical Analysis

## The Earth's Atmosphere and Resources

## Practice Exam Papers

## Answers

## Periodic Table

**1** The chemical sodium chloride is more commonly known as 'salt' (i.e. the food flavouring).

Sodium chloride can be made in the laboratory by reacting sodium with chlorine gas. Salt is very soluble in water.

**(a)** Give the chemical symbols for the two elements present in sodium chloride. Use the periodic table on page 88 to help you. (2)

.......................................................................................................................................................

**(b)** Write a word equation to show the reaction between sodium and chlorine to produce sodium chloride. (2)

.......................................................................................................................................................

.......................................................................................................................................................

**(c)** Is sodium chloride a mixture or a compound? Explain your answer. (2)

.......................................................................................................................................................

.......................................................................................................................................................

**(d)** When salt dissolves in water, does it form a mixture or a compound? Explain your answer. (2)

.......................................................................................................................................................

.......................................................................................................................................................

**(e)** A student wants to separate salt and water from salty water. Which two methods of separation listed below would be appropriate for the student to use? Tick the relevant box or boxes. (2)

Filtration ☐   Simple distillation ☐

Crystallisation ☐   Chromatography ☐

**For more help on this topic, see Letts GCSE Chemistry Revision Guide pages 4–5**

**1** One of the early representations of the atom, the 'plum pudding' model, was further developed in light of Rutherford, Geiger and Marsden's scattering experiment. This led to the conclusion that the positive charge of an atom is contained within a small volume known as the nucleus. Niels Bohr improved this model and it is this model that forms the basis of the way in which we represent the structure of atoms today.

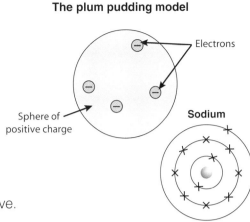

**The plum pudding model**

Electrons

Sphere of positive charge

Sodium

The plum pudding version of an atom is shown above.

Today, an atom such as sodium is represented by a diagram like the one above.

**(a)** Give two differences between the 'plum pudding' model of an atom and today's model. (2)

......................................................................................................................................

......................................................................................................................................

**(b)** What observation in Rutherford, Geiger and Marsden's scattering experiment led them to conclude that the positive charge of an atom was contained in a small volume? (1)

......................................................................................................................................

**(c)** What improvements did Niels Bohr make to the nuclear model and what evidence did he have to support these changes? (2)

......................................................................................................................................

......................................................................................................................................

**(d)** James Chadwick developed the idea that the nucleus of an atom contains protons and neutrons.

Complete the table below showing the properties of the sub-atomic particles. (4)

| Particle | Relative charge | Relative mass |
|----------|-----------------|---------------|
| Proton   | + 1             |               |
| Neutron  |                 | 1             |
| Electron |                 |               |

**(e)** An atom of sodium contains 11 protons, 12 neutrons and 11 electrons.

   **(i)** What is the atomic number of sodium? ................................................................. (1)

   **(ii)** What is the mass number of sodium? ................................................................. (1)

For more help on this topic, see Letts GCSE Chemistry Revision Guide pages 6–7

Atomic structure

Module 2

**1** The diagrams below represent an atom of magnesium and an atom of fluorine:

The electronic structure of magnesium can also be written as 2,8,2

**(a)** How many shells of electrons does a magnesium atom have? (1)

.................................................

**(b)** What is the electronic structure of fluorine? (1)

.................................................

**(c)** In which group of the periodic table would you expect to find fluorine?
Explain your answer. (2)

..............................................................................................................................

..............................................................................................................................

**2** Dmitri Mendeleev is often referred to as the father of the periodic table, as he was instrumental in its construction.

Mendeleev placed the metals lithium and sodium in the same group of the periodic table.

**(a)** How are the elements arranged in the periodic table? (1)

..............................................................................................................................

**(b)** Explain why Mendeleev placed sodium and lithium in the same group of the periodic table. (1)

..............................................................................................................................

**(c)** Give two characteristic properties of metals. (2)

..............................................................................................................................

..............................................................................................................................

**For more help on this topic, see Letts GCSE Chemistry Revision Guide pages 8–9**

**1 (a)** Explain why the noble gases are chemically inert. (2)

.......................................................................................................................................

.......................................................................................................................................

**(b)** What is the trend in boiling point as the relative atomic mass of the noble gases

increases? ............................................................................... (1)

**2** The element sodium reacts vigorously with water. When universal indicator solution is added to the resulting solution a colour change is observed.

**(a)** Write a balanced symbol equation for the reaction between sodium and water. (2)

.......................................................................................................................................

**(b)** What colour would universal indicator solution turn when it is added to the resulting

solution? Explain your answer. (2)

.......................................................................................................................................

.......................................................................................................................................

**(c)** The element potassium reacts more vigorously with water than sodium. Explain why. (2)

.......................................................................................................................................

.......................................................................................................................................

**3** Sodium reacts with bromine gas as shown by the equation below:

.........$Na_{(s)}$ + .........$Cl_{2(g)}$ ⟶ .........$NaCl_{(s)}$

**(a)** Balance the above equation. (2)

**(b)** What type of bonding is present in sodium chloride (NaCl)? (1)

.......................................................................................

**(c)** When chlorine gas is bubbled through sodium bromide solution a chemical reaction

occurs. Write a word equation for this reaction. (2)

.......................................................................................................................................

**(d)** What name is given to the type of reaction that occurs when chlorine gas reacts with

sodium bromide solution? Explain why the reaction occurs. (2)

.......................................................................................................................................

.......................................................................................................................................

**For more help on this topic, see Letts GCSE Chemistry Revision Guide pages 10–11**

Groups 0, 1 and 7     Module 4

**1** The table below shows information about two metals, L and M.

One of the metals is a transition metal and the other is in group 1.

| | Metal L | Metal M |
|---|---|---|
| Melting point (°C) | 181 | 1538 |
| Density (g cm$^{-3}$) | 0.53 | 7.9 |

**(a)** Which of the two metals is the transition metal? Explain your answer. (2)

..................................................................................................................................................

..................................................................................................................................................

**(b)** Complete the sentence below by inserting the correct word.

Transition metals are ........................................ reactive than group 1 metals. (1)

**(c)** Name the only transition metal that has a melting point below room temperature. (1)

..................................................................................................................................................

**2** Iron(II) chloride and iron(III) chloride are both soluble in water.

Green          Brown

**(a)** State the property of transition metals that is demonstrated by the above image. (1)

..................................................................................................................................................

**(b)** Iron is added to the reaction vessel that produces ammonia ($NH_3$) from nitrogen ($N_2$) and hydrogen ($H_2$).

Explain why this is done. (2)

..................................................................................................................................................

..................................................................................................................................................

**For more help on this topic, see Letts GCSE Chemistry Revision Guide pages 12–13**

**1** Consider the structures of sodium (Na), chlorine (Cl₂) and sodium chloride (NaCl).

Draw arrows from each substance to its correct structure. One structure will not have an arrow drawn to it. (3)

| Sodium | |
| Chlorine | |
| Sodium chloride | |

• Ionic

• Simple molecular

• Giant molecular

• Metallic

**2** Calcium reacts with oxygen to form calcium oxide. The bonding in calcium oxide is ionic.

**(a)** Complete the diagrams below to show the electronic configurations and charges of the calcium and oxygen ions. (2)

**(b)** State the charges on each ion. (2)

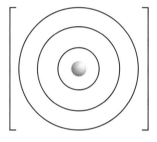 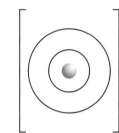

.............................................................

.............................................................

**3** **(a)** Draw a dot-and-cross diagram to show the structure of HCl. (1)

**(b)** The dot-and-cross diagram for a molecule of oxygen is show below.

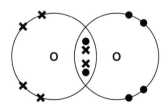

How many covalent bonds are there between the two oxygen atoms? (1)

.........................................................................

For more help on this topic, see Letts GCSE Chemistry Revision Guide pages 16–17

**1** The structure of calcium oxide is shown below.

– Negatively charged oxide ions

+ Positively charged calcium ions

**(a)** What force holds the ions in place in calcium oxide? (1)

......................................................................................................................................

**(b)** What is the empirical formula of calcium oxide? Explain your answer. (2)

......................................................................................................................................

......................................................................................................................................

**2** The structure of a covalent compound is shown below.

**(a)** Name this type of structure. ................................................................... (1)

**(b)** What is the empirical formula of this structure? Explain your answer. (2)

......................................................................................................................................

......................................................................................................................................

**3** The structure of boron nitride is shown below.

○ Boron atoms
● Nitrogen atoms

What type of structure does boron nitride have? Explain your answer. (2)

......................................................................................................................................

......................................................................................................................................

**For more help on this topic, see Letts GCSE Chemistry Revision Guide pages 18–19**

**1** Solids, liquids and gases are the three main states of matter. The three physical states of matter can be easily interconverted.

**(a)** Draw a diagram to show the arrangement of particles in a solid. (2)

**(b)** What forces are broken when a solid turns into a liquid? (1)

..................................................................................................................................

**2** Consider the table below, which provides information about the physical properties of two materials.

| | Material A | Material B |
|---|---|---|
| Melting point/°C | 801 | 3730 |
| Electrical conductivity of solid | Poor | Poor |
| Electrical conductivity of liquid | Good | Poor |

**(a)** Material A has a giant ionic structure. Explain how this can be deduced from the table. (1)

..................................................................................................................................

**(b)** Explain why material A is a poor conductor of electricity in the solid state. (2)

..................................................................................................................................

..................................................................................................................................

**(c)** Deduce the structure of material B. Explain your answer. (2)

..................................................................................................................................

..................................................................................................................................

**(d)** Explain why material B is a poor conductor of electricity in both the solid and liquid states. (2)

..................................................................................................................................

..................................................................................................................................

**For more help on this topic, see Letts GCSE Chemistry Revision Guide pages 20–21**

1 The diagram shows the structure of a metal such as magnesium.

With reference to the diagram, explain the following:

Free electron

Positive metal ion

(a) Why metals are malleable (i.e. able to be bent and shaped). (2)

..............................................................................................

..............................................................................................

(b) Why metals usually have high melting points. (2)

..............................................................................................

..............................................................................................

(c) Why metals are good conductors of electricity. (2)

..............................................................................................

..............................................................................................

2 Most metals in everyday use are alloys, such as steel.

(a) What is an alloy? (1)

..............................................................................................

(b) With reference to its structure, explain why most alloys are harder than pure metals. (2)

..............................................................................................

..............................................................................................

3 This question is about different structures of carbon.

(a) Give two uses of fullerenes. (2)

..............................................................................................

..............................................................................................

(b) State two properties of fullerenes. (2)

..............................................................................................

..............................................................................................

(c) What is the difference between a fullerene and a carbon nanotube? (1)

..............................................................................................

**For more help on this topic, see Letts GCSE Chemistry Revision Guide pages 22–23**

**1** Draw lines to match the particles below to their size. (3)

**Name of particle**

| Nanoparticles |
| Fine particles (PM$_{2.5}$) |
| Coarse particles/dust (PM$_{10}$) |

**Diameter of particle**

| Between $1 \times 10^{-5}$ and $2.5 \times 10^{-6}$ m |
| Between $1 \times 10^{-7}$ and $2.5 \times 10^{-6}$ m |
| Less than $1 \times 10^{-7}$ m (100 nm) |

**2** Nanoparticles sometimes have properties that are different from larger amounts of the same material.

**(a)** Explain why this is true. (1)

.................................................................................................................................................

**(b)** Outline the main advantage of this. (1)

.................................................................................................................................................

.................................................................................................................................................

**3** Nanoparticles typically have properties that differ from larger quantities of the same material. One explanation for this is the different surface area to volume ratios.

**(a)** What effect on the surface area to volume ratio does decreasing particle size have? (1)

.................................................................................................................................................

**(b)** Other than use in sun creams, give two uses of nanoparticles. (2)

.................................................................................................................................................

.................................................................................................................................................

**(c)** Outline the advantages and potential disadvantages of using nanoparticles in sun creams. (4)

.................................................................................................................................................

.................................................................................................................................................

.................................................................................................................................................

.................................................................................................................................................

.................................................................................................................................................

**Bulk and surface properties of matter, including nanoparticles**

**Module 10**

**For more help on this topic, see Letts GCSE Chemistry Revision Guide pages 24–25**

**1** Consider the equation below.

$$2Al_{(s)} + Fe_2O_{3(l)} \longrightarrow Al_2O_{3(s)} + 2Fe_{(l)}$$

**(a)** With reference to the above equation, what do you understand by the term 'conservation of mass'? (1)

...............................................................................................................................................

**(b)** Complete the table below by filling in the relative atomic ($A_r$) or formula ($M_r$) mass of each substance in the equation. (4)

| Substance | $A_r / M_r$ |
|-----------|-------------|
| Al | |
| $Fe_2O_3$ | |
| $Al_2O_3$ | |
| Fe | |

**2** Magnesium oxide can be made by heating magnesium in air or by the thermal decomposition of magnesium carbonate.

**(a)** Explain why the mass of magnesium increases when it is burnt in air. (2)

...............................................................................................................................................

...............................................................................................................................................

**(b)** Write a balanced symbol equation for the reaction that occurs when magnesium is heated in air. (2)

...............................................................................................................................................

**(c)** Explain why the mass of magnesium carbonate decreases when it is heated in air. (2)

...............................................................................................................................................

...............................................................................................................................................

**(d)** Write a balanced symbol equation for the thermal decomposition of magnesium carbonate. (2)

...............................................................................................................................................

**For more help on this topic, see Letts GCSE Chemistry Revision Guide pages 28–29**

**1** Consider the equation below.

$$4Na_{(s)} + O_{2(g)} \longrightarrow 2Na_2O_{(s)}$$

**(a)** How many atoms are present in 4 moles of sodium? (1)

.................................................................................................................................

**(b)** What is the mass of 4 moles of Na? (1)

.................................................................................................................................

**(c)** How many moles are present in 11.5 g of sodium? (1)

.................................................................................................................................

**HT** **(d)** What mass of sodium oxide is formed when 11.5 g of sodium reacts with oxygen? (2)

.................................................................................................................................

.................................................................................................................................

**2** A hydrocarbon contains 6 g of carbon and 1 g of hydrogen.

**(a)** Calculate the empirical formula of this hydrocarbon. (3)

**(b)** The relative formula mass of this hydrocarbon is 98.

Determine its molecular formula. (2)

.................................................................................................................................

.................................................................................................................................

For more help on this topic, see Letts GCSE Chemistry Revision Guide pages 30–31

Moles and masses

Module 12

**1** Ethanol is a chemical present in alcoholic drinks. In its pure form, it is also a solvent.

Ethanol can be made...

- by the fermentation of sugars, e.g. glucose ($C_6H_{12}O_6$)

  $C_6H_{12}O_{6(aq)} \longrightarrow 2C_2H_5OH_{(aq)} + 2CO_{2(g)}$

**or**

- by reacting ethene ($C_2H_4$) with steam

  $C_2H_{4(g)} + H_2O_{(g)} \longrightarrow C_2H_5OH_{(g)}$

The relative formula mass ($M_r$) of ethene is 28 and of ethanol is 46.

**(a)** Calculate the percentage yield when, during a fermentation experiment, the mass of ethanol obtained was 11.5 g and the expected mass was 15.0 g. (2)

.............................................................................................................................................

.............................................................................................................................................

**(b)** In an experiment, 7 g of ethene reacted with an excess of steam to form 11 g of ethanol.

**(i)** Calculate the number of moles of ethene reacting. (2)

.............................................................................................................................................

.............................................................................................................................................

**(ii)** How many moles of ethanol would be expected to be formed?
Explain your answer. (2)

.............................................................................................................................................

.............................................................................................................................................

**(iii)** What mass of ethanol would be expected to be formed? (2)

.............................................................................................................................................

**(iv)** Calculate the percentage yield. (2)

.............................................................................................................................................

.............................................................................................................................................

**(c)** Calculate the atom economy for both methods of producing ethanol. (2)

.............................................................................................................................................

.............................................................................................................................................

**For more help on this topic, see Letts GCSE Chemistry Revision Guide pages 32–33**

**HT** **1** During a titration, a student adds acid to a known volume of alkali until neutralisation occurs. The alkali has an indicator added to it.

**(a)** Name the piece of apparatus used to measure out the known volume of alkali. (1)

........................................................................................................................................................

**(b)** Name the piece of apparatus used to add the acid to the alkali. (1)

........................................................................................................................................................

**(c)** How will the student know when the alkali has been neutralised? (1)

........................................................................................................................................................

**HT** **2** In a titration, 23.80 $cm^3$ of 0.2 $mol/dm^3$ lithium hydroxide (LiOH) solution reacted with 25.0 $cm^3$ of hydrochloric acid (HCl) of unknown concentration.

The equation for the reaction is shown here: $LiOH_{(aq)} + HCl_{(aq)} \longrightarrow LiCl_{(aq)} + H_2O_{(l)}$

**(a)** Calculate the number of moles of lithium hydroxide (LiOH) used in each titration. (2)

........................................................................................................................................................

........................................................................................................................................................

**(b)** How many moles of hydrochloric acid (HCl) were present in the 25.0 $cm^3$ portion? Explain your answer. (2)

........................................................................................................................................................

........................................................................................................................................................

**(c)** Using your answer to part **b**, calculate the concentration of the hydrochloric acid solution in $mol/dm^3$. (2)

........................................................................................................................................................

........................................................................................................................................................

**(d)** Use your answer to part **c** to work out the concentration of the hydrochloric acid solution in $g/dm^3$. (2)

........................................................................................................................................................

**(e)** What mass of hydrochloric acid was present in the 25.0 $cm^3$ portion? (2)

........................................................................................................................................................

........................................................................................................................................................

**HT** **Moles, solutions and masses**

**Module 14**

**For more help on this topic, see Letts GCSE Chemistry Revision Guide pages 34–35**

**HT** **1** Magnesium reacts with oxygen according to the equation below:

$$2Mg_{(s)} + O_{2(g)} \longrightarrow 2MgO_{(s)}$$

**(a)** A scientist reacted 120 cm³ of oxygen (at room temperature and pressure) with magnesium. How many moles of oxygen did the scientist use? (2)

..................................................................................................................................

..................................................................................................................................

**(b)** Another scientist reacted 6 g of magnesium with oxygen. Calculate the volume of oxygen required (at room temperature and pressure) to react with this amount of magnesium. (3)

..................................................................................................................................

..................................................................................................................................

..................................................................................................................................

**HT** **2** Lead forms the following oxides: PbO, $PbO_2$ and $Pb_3O_4$. In an experiment, 41.4 g of lead reacts with 3.2 g of oxygen to form 44.6 g of PbO.

Complete the table below to work out the equation for the reaction of lead with oxygen to form lead oxide. (4)

| Chemical | Pb | O₂ | PbO |
|---|---|---|---|
| Mass from question/g | 41.4 | 3.2 | 44.6 |
| $A_r$ or $M_r$ | 207 | | 223 |
| Moles $= \dfrac{\text{mass}}{M_r}$ | $\dfrac{41.4}{207}$ $= 0.2$ | | |
| ÷ smallest | | | |

Balanced equation: ............ Pb + O₂ $\longrightarrow$ ............ PbO

**For more help on this topic, see Letts GCSE Chemistry Revision Guide pages 36–37**

**1** Calcium reacts with oxygen present in the air to form calcium oxide.

**(a)** Write a word equation for this reaction. (2)

.......................................................................................................................................

**(b)** Explain why this is an oxidation reaction. (2)

.......................................................................................................................................

.......................................................................................................................................

**(c)** Name a metal that could be used to displace calcium from calcium oxide.
Explain your choice of metal. (2)

.......................................................................................................................................

.......................................................................................................................................

**(d)** Write a word equation for this reaction. (2)

.......................................................................................................................................

**(e)** In your equation from part **d**, give the name of the substance that has been reduced. (1)

.......................................................................................................................................

**2** Many metals are found in the Earth's crust as ores. For example, haematite is an ore containing iron(III) oxide ($Fe_2O_3$); bauxite is an ore containing aluminium oxide ($Al_2O_3$). Both metals can be extracted from their ores by reduction.

**(a)** What process is used to extract metals above carbon in the reactivity series from

their ores? ................................................................................................................ (1)

**(b)** When iron(III) oxide is reduced by carbon, iron and carbon dioxide are formed.
Write a balanced symbol equation for this reaction. (2)

.......................................................................................................................................

**HT** **(c)** In the extraction of aluminium the following equation occurs: $Al^{3+} + 3e^- \longrightarrow Al$

Is this an oxidation or reduction reaction? Explain your answer. (3)

.......................................................................................................................................

.......................................................................................................................................

**HT** **(d)** Aluminium can also be formed by reacting a reactive metal such as potassium.
An ionic equation for this reaction would be: $3K + Al^{3+} \longrightarrow Al + 3K^+$
Which substance is oxidised in this reaction? Explain your answer. (2)

.......................................................................................................................................

.......................................................................................................................................

**For more help on this topic, see Letts GCSE Chemistry Revision Guide pages 40–41**

**1** Zinc, zinc oxide and zinc carbonate all react with acids.

**(a)** Name the salt formed when zinc, zinc oxide and zinc carbonate react with sulfuric acid.

(1)

...................................................................................................................................................

**(b)** Write a word equation for the reaction between zinc oxide and hydrochloric acid. (2)

...................................................................................................................................................

**(c)** Name and give the formula of the gas formed when zinc carbonate reacts with nitric acid.

(2)

...................................................................................................................................................

**HT** **(d)** The ionic equation for the reaction between calcium and acid is:

$$Ca_{(s)} + 2H^+_{(aq)} \longrightarrow Ca^{2+}_{(aq)} + H_{2(g)}$$

**(i)** Which substance is oxidised in the above reaction? (1)

..............................................................................................

**(ii)** Which substance is reduced? (1)

..............................................................................................

**HT** **(e)** In terms of electrons, what is meant by an oxidation reaction? (2)

...................................................................................................................................................

**2** Copper(II) oxide (CuO) reacts with sulfuric acid to make the soluble salt copper(II) sulfate according to the equation below.

$$CuO_{(s)} + H_2SO_{4(aq)} \longrightarrow CuSO_{4(aq)} + H_2O_{(l)}$$

**(a)** Describe the steps you would take to prepare a sample of solid copper(II) sulfate, starting from copper(II) oxide and sulfuric acid solution.

(3)

...................................................................................................................................................

...................................................................................................................................................

...................................................................................................................................................

**(b)** The salt sodium nitrate can be formed by the reaction of sodium carbonate with an acid. Name this acid.

(1)

...................................................................................................................................................

**(c)** Is sodium nitrate a soluble or insoluble salt? ................................................................... (1)

**For more help on this topic, see Letts GCSE Chemistry Revision Guide pages 42–43**

**1** Hydrogen chloride (HCl) and ethanoic acid (CH$_3$COOH) both dissolve in water to form acidic solutions.

**(a)** What is the pH range of acids? (1)

.....................................................................................................................................

**(b)** Give the name and formula for the ion present in solutions of hydrogen chloride and ethanoic acid. (2)

.....................................................................................................................................

**(c)** What is the common name for hydrogen chloride solution? (1)

.....................................................................................................................................

**(d)** Acids can be neutralised by reaction with an alkali such as sodium hydroxide.

Write an ionic equation for the reaction that occurs when an acid is neutralised by an alkali. Include state symbols in your equation. (2)

.....................................................................................................................................

**HT** **2** Ethanoic acid is a key ingredient in vinegar. It is a weak acid. Nitric acid is a strong acid.

**(a)** What is the difference between a weak acid and a strong acid? (2)

.....................................................................................................................................

.....................................................................................................................................

**(b)** Write a balanced symbol equation for the dissociation of ethanoic acid in water. (2)

.....................................................................................................................................

**(c)** Will a solution of nitric acid of the same concentration as a solution of ethanoic acid have a higher or lower pH?

Explain your answer. (2)

.....................................................................................................................................

.....................................................................................................................................

**(d)** What happens to the pH value of an acid when it is diluted by a factor of 10? (2)

.....................................................................................................................................

.....................................................................................................................................

**For more help on this topic, see Letts GCSE Chemistry Revision Guide pages 44–45**

**1** The diagram shows how a molten salt such as lead(II) bromide ($PbBr_2$) can be electrolysed. Lead(II) bromide consists of $Pb^{2+}$ and $Br^-$ ions.

Molten lead(II) bromide

**(a)** What general name is given to positive ions? (1)

.............................................................................................

**(b)** What general name is given to negative ions?

............................................................................. (1)

**(c)** Explain why the lead(II) bromide needs to be molten. (2)

.............................................................................................

.............................................................................................

**HT** **(d)** At the anode, the following reaction occurs: $2Br^- \longrightarrow Br_2 + 2e^-$

Is this an oxidation or a reduction reaction? Explain your answer. (2)

.............................................................................................

.............................................................................................

**2** **(a)** The table below shows the products at each electrode when the following solutions are electrolysed. Some answers have already been filled in. Complete the table. (6)

| Solution | Product at anode | Product at cathode |
|---|---|---|
| NaCl | $H_2$ | |
| $KNO_3$ | | |
| $CuSO_4$ | | |
| Water diluted with sulfuric acid | | $O_2$ |

**(b)** Explain why sodium is not formed at the cathode when aqueous sodium chloride is electrolysed. (2)

.............................................................................................

.............................................................................................

**HT** **(c)** Write a half-equation for the formation of oxygen at the anode in the electrolysis of water diluted with sulfuric acid. (2)

.............................................................................................

**For more help on this topic, see Letts GCSE Chemistry Revision Guide pages 46–47**

**1** When methane burns in air an exothermic reaction takes place. The equation for the reaction is shown here:

$$CH_{4(g)} + 2O_{2(g)} \longrightarrow CO_{2(g)} + 2H_2O_{(l)}$$

(a) On the axes, draw and label a reaction profile for an exothermic reaction. Label the reactants, products, activation energy and ΔH. (5)

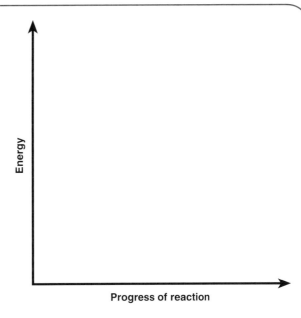

Energy

Progress of reaction

(b) In terms of bond energies, explain why this reaction is exothermic. (2)

.................................................................................................

.................................................................................................

(c) Give an example of an endothermic chemical reaction. (1)

.................................................................................................

**2** Hydrogen peroxide ($H_2O_2$) decomposes in air to form water and oxygen. The diagram below shows this reaction by displaying all of the bonds present in the reactants and products.

$$2 \quad \begin{matrix} H \\ \diagdown \\ O-O \\ \diagdown \\ H \end{matrix} \longrightarrow 2 \ H-O-H \ + \ O=O$$

The table states the bond energy values of the bonds present in hydrogen peroxide, water and oxygen.

| Bond | Bond energy kJ/mol |
|------|--------------------|
| H–O | 463 |
| O–O | 146 |
| O=O | 496 |

For the decomposition of hydrogen peroxide:

(a) Calculate ΔH for the reaction. (3)

.................................................................................................

.................................................................................................

(b) Is this reaction exothermic or endothermic? Explain your answer. (2)

.................................................................................................

.................................................................................................

**For more help on this topic, see Letts GCSE Chemistry Revision Guide pages 48–49**

Energy changes in reactions

Module 20

Everyday batteries, like the ones shown below, are actually chemical 'cells' used to provide electrical energy. Fuel cells are also sources of energy and were used in the space shuttle.

**1** Describe the internal structure of a chemical cell. (2)

.......................................................................................................................................................

.......................................................................................................................................................

**2** What causes a current to flow in a chemical cell? (2)

.......................................................................................................................................................

.......................................................................................................................................................

**3** Outline two ways in which the voltage produced by a chemical cell can be varied. (2)

.......................................................................................................................................................

.......................................................................................................................................................

**4** Why do alkaline 'batteries' eventually stop producing an electric current? (1)

.......................................................................................................................................................

.......................................................................................................................................................

**5** What is the main difference between a fuel cell and a chemical cell? (1)

.......................................................................................................................................................

**6** Write the overall equation for the reaction occurring in a hydrogen fuel cell. (2)

.......................................................................................................................................................

**For more help on this topic, see Letts GCSE Chemistry Revision Guide pages 50–51**

**1** A pupil was investigating the effect of temperature on the rate of reaction between aqueous sodium thiosulfate with dilute hydrochloric acid. When the acid is added to the sodium thiosulfate solution, a precipitate of sulfur gradually forms. The pupil recorded the time taken for a cross written on a piece of paper to disappear from view.

The experiment was repeated at different temperatures. The results are shown in the table below.

Experimenter looking down through the flask

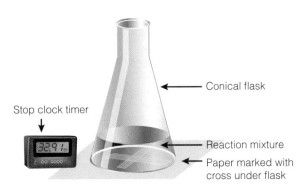

Conical flask

Stop clock timer

Reaction mixture

Paper marked with cross under flask

| Temperature (°C) | Time taken for cross to disappear from view (s) |
|---|---|
| 15 | 70 |
| 25 | 44 |
| 40 | 30 |
| 55 | 22 |
| 70 | 14 |

**(a)** At which temperature was the reaction the fastest? ........................................................ (1)

**(b)** Suggest how the rate of this reaction at 30°C will change when the concentration of hydrochloric acid is increased. Explain your answer. (2)

................................................................................................................................................

................................................................................................................................................

**2** A student investigating the rate of reaction between magnesium and hydrochloric acid carried out two experiments: one using magnesium ribbon and the other using magnesium powder.

The equation for the reaction is shown here: $Mg_{(s)} + 2HCl_{(aq)} \longrightarrow MgCl_{2(aq)} + H_{2(g)}$

In the first experiment, 69 cm³ of hydrogen gas was collected in 46 seconds. In the second experiment, 18 cm³ of hydrogen gas was collected in 10 seconds.

**(a)** Calculate the rate of reaction in both experiments. (3)

................................................................................................................................................

................................................................................................................................................

**(b)** Which experiment was carried out using magnesium powder? Explain your answer. (2)

................................................................................................................................................

**For more help on this topic, see Letts GCSE Chemistry Revision Guide pages 54–55**

**1** One aspect of collision theory states that, for a chemical reaction to occur, the reacting particles must first collide with each other.

**(a)** What else must occur in order for the collision to be successful? (1)

.......................................................................................................................................................

**(b)** Explain how:

**(i)** Increasing the pressure of a gas increases the rate of a reaction. (2)

.......................................................................................................................................................

.......................................................................................................................................................

**(ii)** Increasing the temperature of a solution increases the rate of a reaction. (3)

.......................................................................................................................................................

.......................................................................................................................................................

.......................................................................................................................................................

**(c)** Adding a catalyst to a reaction increases the rate of reaction. Draw, on the diagram below, the reaction profile for the reaction when a catalyst is added. (1)

**(d)** Explain how a catalyst is able to increase the rate of a reaction. (2)

.......................................................................................................................................................

.......................................................................................................................................................

**For more help on this topic, see Letts GCSE Chemistry Revision Guide pages 56–57**

**1** In an experiment, a student heated some blue crystals of hydrated copper(II) sulfate in an evaporating dish.

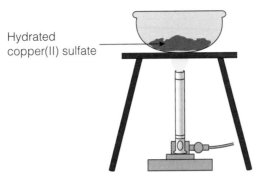

Hydrated copper(II) sulfate

**(a)** State what colour change will be observed during the reaction. (1)

.................................................................................................................................

**(b)** Write a word equation for the change that occurs to the hydrated copper(II) sulfate during this experiment. (2)

.................................................................................................................................

**(c)** Describe what will be observed when water is added to the solid remaining at the end of the experiment. (1)

.................................................................................................................................

**(d)** Is the addition of water an exothermic or endothermic reaction? (1)

.................................................................................................................................

**2** Consider the reaction given here: $2SO_{2(g)} + O_{2(g)} \rightleftharpoons 2SO_{3(g)}$

**(a)** What does the $\rightleftharpoons$ symbol represent? ............................................................... (1)

**(b)** What would be the effect on the yield of $SO_3$ if the above reaction was carried out at a higher pressure? Explain your answer. (3)

.................................................................................................................................

.................................................................................................................................

.................................................................................................................................

**(c)** The forward reaction is exothermic. What would be the effect on the yield of $SO_3$ if the above reaction was carried out at a higher temperature? Explain your answer. (3)

.................................................................................................................................

.................................................................................................................................

.................................................................................................................................

**For more help on this topic, see Letts GCSE Chemistry Revision Guide pages 58–59**

**1** Crude oil is separated into its constituent components by fractional distillation. A fractionating column is used to carry out fractional distillation.

A diagram of a fractionating column is shown here.

Refinery gases

Gasoline (petrol)

X

Diesel oil

Fuel oil

Heated crude oil →

Bitumen

**(a)** What is the name of the fraction labelled as 'X'? (1)

...............................................................................

**(b)** As you go down the fractionating column, what happens to the boiling point of the fractions? (1)

...............................................................................

**(c)** Explain how crude oil is separated in a fractionating column. (3)

...............................................................................................................................

...............................................................................................................................

...............................................................................................................................

**2** Most of the hydrocarbons found in crude oil are alkanes.

**(a)** What is the general formula of alkanes? (1)

...............................................................................................................................

**(b)** In the space below, draw the displayed formula for propane. (1)

**(c)** Write a balanced symbol equation for the complete combustion of propane. (2)

...............................................................................................................................

...............................................................................................................................

**For more help on this topic, see Letts GCSE Chemistry Revision Guide pages 62–63**

**1** This question is about the alkene propene ($C_3H_6$).

**(a)** What is the general formula of alkenes? (1)

.................................................................................................................................

**(b)** In the space below, draw the displayed formula of propene. (2)

**(c)** With reference to your diagram in part **b**, explain why alkenes are unsaturated. (2)

.................................................................................................................................

.................................................................................................................................

**(d)** Write a balanced symbol equation for the complete combustion of propene. (2)

.................................................................................................................................

**(e)** Draw the displayed formula of the molecule formed when propene reacts with hydrogen. (1)

**2** Cracking is a method of converting long-chain hydrocarbons into shorter, more useful hydrocarbons.

**(a)** Name a catalyst used to crack hydrocarbons. (1)

.................................................................................................................................

**(b)** The equation for a reaction that occurs during this process is:

$$C_{12}H_{26} \longrightarrow C_2H_4 + C_6H_{12} + X$$

In the balanced equation, what is the molecular formula of X? (1)

.................................................................................................................................

For more help on this topic, see Letts GCSE Chemistry Revision Guide pages 64–65

Cracking and alkenes

Module 26

**1** The alcohol ethanol and ethanoic acid, which is a carboxylic acid, react together to form an ester. The displayed formula of ethanol is shown here.

```
    H   H
    |   |
H — C — C — O — H
    |   |
    H   H
```

**(a)** What functional group is present in alcohols?............................................................................... (1)

**(b)** What is the structural formula of ethanol? (1)

................................................................................................................................................................

**(c)** State two properties of alcohols. (2)

................................................................................................................................................................

................................................................................................................................................................

**(d)** Other than making esters, state two uses of alcohols. (2)

................................................................................................................................................................

................................................................................................................................................................

**(e)** In the space below, draw the displayed formula of ethanoic acid. (1)

**(f)** State two chemical properties of carboxylic acids, such as ethanoic acid. (2)

................................................................................................................................................................

................................................................................................................................................................

**(g)** How can ethanol be converted into ethanoic acid? (1)

................................................................................................................................................................

**(h)** Name the ester formed when ethanol reacts with ethanoic acid. (1)

................................................................................................................................................................

**(i)** In the space below, draw the displayed formula of the ester formed from the reaction between ethanol and ethanoic acid. (1)

**For more help on this topic, see Letts GCSE Chemistry Revision Guide pages 66–67**

**1** Poly(ethene) is a man-made polymer that has many uses in everyday life.

**(a)** Name the monomer used to make poly(ethene). (1)

.........................................................................................................................

**(b)** In the space below, draw the displayed formula for this monomer. (1)

**(c)** What type of polymer is poly(ethene)? (1)

.........................................................................................................................

**(d)** What feature of the monomer means that it is able to undergo this type of polymerisation? (1)

.........................................................................................................................

**(e)** State two uses of poly(ethene) and state what properties of poly(ethene) make it suitable for these uses. (3)

.........................................................................................................................

......................................................................................................... (2)

**2** Many naturally occurring materials, e.g. proteins and starch, are formed by condensation polymerisation.

**(a)** What is meant by the term 'condensation polymerisation'? (2)

.........................................................................................................................

.........................................................................................................................

**(b)** Proteins are made from amino acids. What two functional groups are present in amino acids? (2)

.........................................................................................................................

.........................................................................................................................

**(c)** What is the monomer used to make starch? (1)

.........................................................................................................................

**For more help on this topic, see Letts GCSE Chemistry Revision Guide pages 68–69**

**1** Paint and household cleaning chemicals are typical examples of everyday chemical formulations.

**(a)** What is a formulation? (1)

.........................................................................................................................................

**(b)** Are formulations chemically pure? Explain your answer. (2)

.........................................................................................................................................

.........................................................................................................................................

**(c)** Give one other example of a type of formulation. (1)

.........................................................................................................................................

**2** Pen ink is typically a mixture of dyes. The individual dyes in pen ink can be separated by paper chromatography. The chromatogram below is for an unknown ink 'X' and the standard colours blue, red and green.

**(a)** What is the mobile phase in paper chromatography? (1)

.........................................................................................................................................

**(b)** Which colours are present in ink X? Explain your answer. (2)

.........................................................................................................................................

.........................................................................................................................................

**(c)** Calculate the $R_f$ for the blue ink. (2)

.........................................................................................................................................

.........................................................................................................................................

**(d)** The sample of ink could also have been separated using gas chromatography. State one advantage that gas chromatography has over paper chromatography. (1)

.........................................................................................................................................

**For more help on this topic, see Letts GCSE Chemistry Revision Guide pages 72–73**

**1** When carbon dioxide gas is bubbled through limewater the following reaction occurs:

$$Ca(OH)_{2(aq)} + CO_{2(g)} \longrightarrow CaCO_{3(s)} + H_2O_{(l)}$$

**(a)** What is the chemical name for limewater? (1)

.............................................................................................................................

**(b)** With reference to the above equation, explain why limewater turns cloudy when
carbon dioxide is bubbled through it. (2)

.............................................................................................................................

.............................................................................................................................

**2** **(a)** Describe what would be observed when moist blue litmus paper is added to a
gas jar containing chlorine gas. (2)

.............................................................................................................................

.............................................................................................................................

**(b)** Is chlorine an acidic or alkaline gas?

What evidence is there to support your answer? (2)

.............................................................................................................................

.............................................................................................................................

**3** Hydrogen and oxygen gases are both colourless, odourless gases.

**(a)** What is the chemical test and observation for hydrogen gas? (2)

.............................................................................................................................

.............................................................................................................................

**(b)** What is the chemical test and observation for oxygen gas? (2)

.............................................................................................................................

.............................................................................................................................

**(c)** When hydrogen gas burns in air it reacts with oxygen to form water. Write a balanced
symbol equation for the reaction taking place. (2)

.............................................................................................................................

.............................................................................................................................

**Identification of gases**

**Module 30**

**For more help on this topic, see Letts GCSE Chemistry Revision Guide pages 74–75**

**1** Draw lines to match the different flame test colours produced by some metal ions. The first one has been done for you. (4)

| Metal ion | Flame test colour |
|-----------|-------------------|
| K⁺ | Brick red |
| Cu²⁺ | Crimson red |
| Li⁺ | Lilac |
| Ca²⁺ | Yellow |
| Na⁺ | Blue/green |

**2** Sodium hydroxide can be used to confirm the presence of some metal cations by precipitation reactions.

**(a)** What is a precipitation reaction? (2)

.......................................................................................................................................................

.......................................................................................................................................................

**(b)** What will be observed when sodium hydroxide solution is added to a solution containing $Cu^{2+}$ ions? (1)

.......................................................................................................................................................

**(c)** Write an ionic equation (including state symbols) for the reaction occurring in part **b**. (2)

.......................................................................................................................................................

**(d)** Both $Mg^{2+}$ ions and $Al^{3+}$ ions give a white precipitate upon the addition of sodium hydroxide solution. Explain how sodium hydroxide solution can be used to distinguish between $Mg^{2+}$ ions and $Al^{3+}$ ions. (2)

.......................................................................................................................................................

.......................................................................................................................................................

**(e)** Explain how sodium hydroxide can be used to distinguish between $Fe^{2+}$ and $Fe^{3+}$ ions. (2)

.......................................................................................................................................................

.......................................................................................................................................................

**(f)** Sodium hydroxide is also involved in confirming the presence of ammonium ($NH_4^+$) ions. Describe how the presence of the ammonium ion in a solution can be confirmed. (3)

.......................................................................................................................................................

.......................................................................................................................................................

.......................................................................................................................................................

**For more help on this topic, see Letts GCSE Chemistry Revision Guide pages 76–77**

**1** This question is about testing for sulfate and carbonate ions. The sulfate ion ($SO_4^{2-}$) can be identified by adding dilute hydrochloric acid followed by barium chloride solution.

**(a)** What colour precipitate is formed in a positive test for the sulfate ion? (1)

.....................................................................................................................................

**(b)** Give the name and formula for this precipitate. (2)

.....................................................................................................................................

**(c)** What is the formula for the carbonate ion? (2)

.....................................................................................................................................

**(d)** Describe how to test for the presence of the carbonate ion in a solid such as calcium carbonate. (3)

.....................................................................................................................................

.....................................................................................................................................

.....................................................................................................................................

**2** The halide ions $Cl^-$, $Br^-$ and $I^-$ can be identified from their solutions by adding nitric acid followed by silver nitrate solution.

**(a)** Explain how this test can be used to distinguish between the $Cl^-$, $Br^-$ and $I^-$ ions. (2)

.....................................................................................................................................

.....................................................................................................................................

**(b)** Write an ionic equation for the reaction that occurs when silver nitrate solution reacts with chloride ions. Include state symbols in your equation. (2)

.....................................................................................................................................

**3** Instrumental methods can be used instead of chemical tests to analyse the composition of substances.

**(a)** Name the instrumental method used to identify metal ions. (1)

.....................................................................................................................................

**(b)** Give two advantages of using an instrumental method of analysis when compared with a chemical test. (2)

.....................................................................................................................................

.....................................................................................................................................

**Identification of anions**

**Module 32**

**For more help on this topic, see Letts GCSE Chemistry Revision Guide pages 78–79**

**1** Many scientists think that the Earth's early atmosphere may have been similar in composition to the gases typically released by volcanoes today.

The pie charts below show the composition of the atmosphere today and the composition of gases released by a volcano.

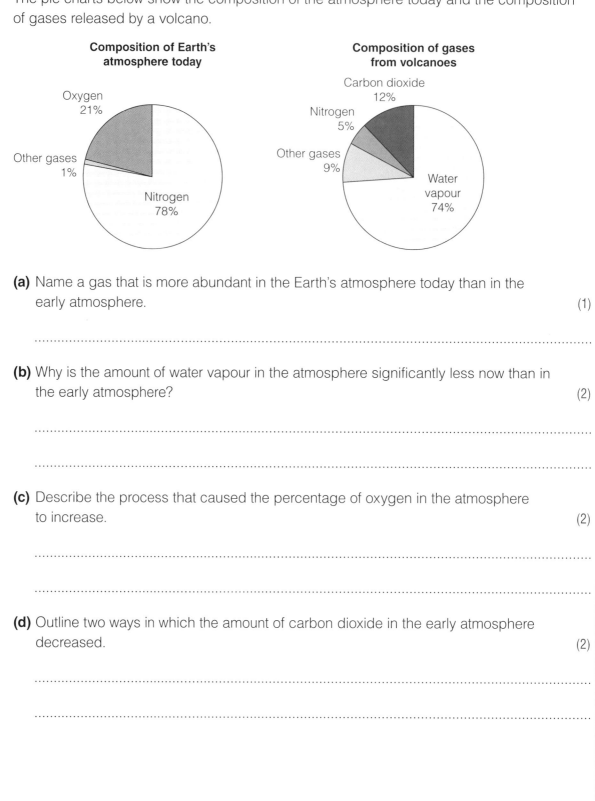

**Composition of Earth's atmosphere today**

Oxygen 21%
Other gases 1%
Nitrogen 78%

**Composition of gases from volcanoes**

Carbon dioxide 12%
Nitrogen 5%
Other gases 9%
Water vapour 74%

**(a)** Name a gas that is more abundant in the Earth's atmosphere today than in the early atmosphere. (1)

...................................................................................................................................................

**(b)** Why is the amount of water vapour in the atmosphere significantly less now than in the early atmosphere? (2)

...................................................................................................................................................

...................................................................................................................................................

**(c)** Describe the process that caused the percentage of oxygen in the atmosphere to increase. (2)

...................................................................................................................................................

...................................................................................................................................................

**(d)** Outline two ways in which the amount of carbon dioxide in the early atmosphere decreased. (2)

...................................................................................................................................................

...................................................................................................................................................

**For more help on this topic, see Letts GCSE Chemistry Revision Guide pages 82–83**

**1** When fossil fuels are burnt, carbon dioxide gas is produced and released into the atmosphere. Some people believe carbon dioxide to be a greenhouse gas.

**(a)** Explain how greenhouse gases maintain the temperature on Earth. (2)

.......................................................................................................................

.......................................................................................................................

**(b)** Name one other greenhouse gas. (1)

.......................................................................................................................

**(c)** Outline two ways in which human activity increases the amounts of greenhouse gases in the atmosphere. (2)

.......................................................................................................................

.......................................................................................................................

**(d)** Why is it not easy to predict the impact of changes on global climate change? (2)

.......................................................................................................................

.......................................................................................................................

**(e)** Describe two potential effects of increasing average global temperature. (2)

.......................................................................................................................

.......................................................................................................................

**(f)** Describe two forms of global action that can be taken to reduce the carbon footprint. (2)

.......................................................................................................................

.......................................................................................................................

**(g)** Outline two potential problems that governments might face when trying to reduce the carbon footprint. (2)

.......................................................................................................................

.......................................................................................................................

**For more help on this topic, see Letts GCSE Chemistry Revision Guide pages 84–85**

**1** The combustion of fossil fuels, e.g. from cars, is a major source of atmospheric pollution.

**(a)** What is meant by a fossil fuel? (1)

.................................................................................................................................................

**(b)** How are carbon and carbon monoxide formed from the combustion of fossil fuels? (1)

.................................................................................................................................................

**(c)** State one harmful effect caused by the release of oxides of nitrogen into
the atmosphere. (1)

.................................................................................................................................................

**(d)** Give two detrimental consequences of releasing particulates into the air. (2)

.................................................................................................................................................

.................................................................................................................................................

**(e)** Explain why carbon monoxide is a toxic gas. (2)

.................................................................................................................................................

.................................................................................................................................................

**(f)** Fuels can contain sulfur as an impurity. Explain how burning this impurity can cause
problems in the environment. (3)

.................................................................................................................................................

.................................................................................................................................................

.................................................................................................................................................

**For more help on this topic, see Letts GCSE Chemistry Revision Guide pages 86–87**

**1** We use the Earth's resources to provide us with warmth, shelter, food and transport. As the Earth is a finite source of resources, we need to ensure that we use them sustainably.

**(a)** What is sustainable development? (1)

........................................................................................................

**(b)** What is meant by the term 'potable water'? (1)

........................................................................................................

**(c)** After identification of an appropriate source of fresh water, what two stages then need to occur to turn this into potable water? (2)

........................................................................................................

........................................................................................................

**(d)** Outline the processes that are used to treat sewage. (3)

........................................................................................................

........................................................................................................

........................................................................................................

**2** Salty water, e.g. seawater, can be desalinated (i.e. treated to reduce its salt content). One such method is distillation.

**(a)** In the space below, draw a labelled diagram to show how seawater can be distilled. Describe how distillation produces desalinated water. (5)

........................................................................................................

........................................................................................................

**(b)** What method of desalination involves the use of membranes? (1)

........................................................................................................

**For more help on this topic, see Letts GCSE Chemistry Revision Guide pages 88–89**

**HT** **1** As we mine more and more of the Earth's natural resources, we need to develop alternative methods of extracting metals such as copper. One such recently developed method is phytomining.

**(a)** What is an ore? (2)

...........................................................................................................................................

...........................................................................................................................................

**(b)** Aside from environmental reasons, why are methods of extracting metals such as phytomining being developed? (2)

...........................................................................................................................................

...........................................................................................................................................

**(c)** State two uses of copper and describe the properties that make it suitable for each purpose. (4)

...........................................................................................................................................

...........................................................................................................................................

**(d)** Describe the process of phytomining. (3)

...........................................................................................................................................

...........................................................................................................................................

...........................................................................................................................................

**(e)** How can bacteria be used to extract metals such as copper? (1)

...........................................................................................................................................

**(f)** Scrap metals, such as iron, can be used to obtain copper from solutions. Write a word equation for the reaction that occurs when iron reacts with copper sulfate solution. (2)

...........................................................................................................................................

**(g)** Why would platinum not be a suitable metal for extracting copper from copper sulfate solution? (1)

...........................................................................................................................................

**(h)** What is the name of the process involving electricity that can be used to extract a metal from a solution of its ions? (1)

...........................................................................................................................................

**For more help on this topic, see Letts GCSE Chemistry Revision Guide pages 90–91**

Life-cycle assessments (LCAs) are carried out to evaluate the environmental impact of products at different stages of the life of a product.

**(a)** Other than transport and distribution, state two other stages of a product life cycle that will be considered when carrying out an LCA. (2)

.................................................................................................................................

.................................................................................................................................

**(b)** State two quantities that are considered when conducting an LCA. (2)

.................................................................................................................................

.................................................................................................................................

**(c)** Explain why the pollution value in a life-cycle value may result in the LCA not being totally objective. (2)

.................................................................................................................................

.................................................................................................................................

**(d)** Why might selective or abbreviated LCAs be misused? (1)

.................................................................................................................................

**HT** **2** The table below shows an example of an LCA for the use of plastic (polythene) and paper shopping bags.

| | Amounts per 1000 bags over the whole LCA | |
| --- | --- | --- |
| | **Paper** | **Plastic (polythene)** |
| Energy use (mJ) | 2590 | 713 |
| Fossil fuel use (kg) | 28 | 12.8 |
| Solid waste (kg) | 34 | 6 |
| Greenhouse gas emissions (kg $CO_2$) | 72 | 36 |
| Fresh water use (litres) | 3387 | 198 |

Based on the above figures, why might some people think that plastic (polythene) bags should be used instead of paper bags? Use information from the table in your answer. (3)

.................................................................................................................................

.................................................................................................................................

.................................................................................................................................

**For more help on this topic, see Letts GCSE Chemistry Revision Guide pages 92–93**

**Life-cycle assessment and recycling**

**Module 38**

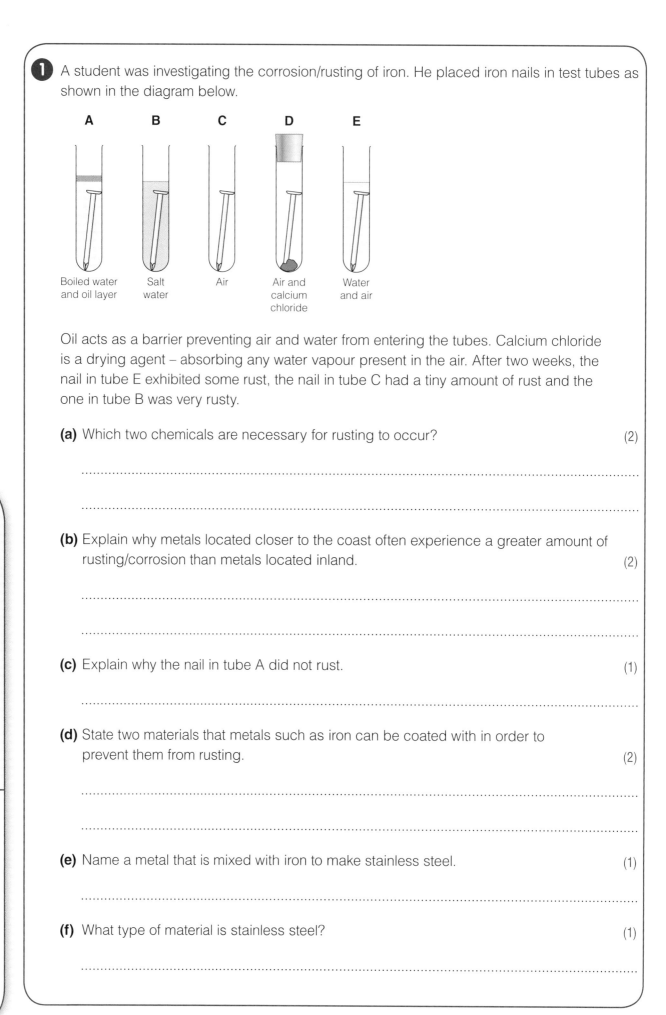

**1** A student was investigating the corrosion/rusting of iron. He placed iron nails in test tubes as shown in the diagram below.

A   B   C   D   E

Boiled water and oil layer    Salt water    Air    Air and calcium chloride    Water and air

Oil acts as a barrier preventing air and water from entering the tubes. Calcium chloride is a drying agent – absorbing any water vapour present in the air. After two weeks, the nail in tube E exhibited some rust, the nail in tube C had a tiny amount of rust and the one in tube B was very rusty.

**(a)** Which two chemicals are necessary for rusting to occur? (2)

.................................................................................................................................................

.................................................................................................................................................

**(b)** Explain why metals located closer to the coast often experience a greater amount of rusting/corrosion than metals located inland. (2)

.................................................................................................................................................

.................................................................................................................................................

**(c)** Explain why the nail in tube A did not rust. (1)

.................................................................................................................................................

**(d)** State two materials that metals such as iron can be coated with in order to prevent them from rusting. (2)

.................................................................................................................................................

.................................................................................................................................................

**(e)** Name a metal that is mixed with iron to make stainless steel. (1)

.................................................................................................................................................

**(f)** What type of material is stainless steel? (1)

.................................................................................................................................................

**For more help on this topic, see Letts GCSE Chemistry Revision Guide pages 94–95**

**1** The Haber process is an important industrial process used to manufacture ammonia ($NH_3$) from nitrogen and hydrogen in the presence of a catalyst. The formation of ammonia is an exothermic process.

This is the equation for the formation of ammonia from its raw materials:

$$N_{2(g)} + 3H_{2(g)} \rightleftharpoons 2NH_{3(g)}$$

**(a)** How are the raw materials obtained? (2)

..........................................................................................................................................

..........................................................................................................................................

**(b)** Name the catalyst used in the manufacture of ammonia. .......................................... (1)

**(c)** Consider the graph below, which shows the effect on the yield of ammonia at different operating temperatures and pressures.

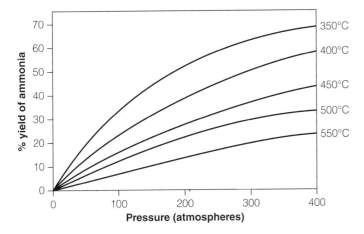

**(i)** Calculate the yield of ammonia in a plant operating at 200 atmospheres pressure

and 500°C. ........................................................................... (1)

**(ii)** With reference to the graph, deduce the effect on the yield of ammonia of increasing temperature. (1)

..........................................................................................................................................

**(d)** State the normal temperature and pressure used in the production of ammonia. (2)

..........................................................................................................................................

**(e)** Explain why a lower temperature is not used, even though it will give a higher yield and cost less. (2)

..........................................................................................................................................

..........................................................................................................................................

**For more help on this topic, see Letts GCSE Chemistry Revision Guide pages 96–97**

# GCSE (9–1)
# Chemistry
**Paper 1**

## Higher tier
Time: 1 hour 45 minutes

**You may use:**
- a calculator
- a ruler
- a periodic table.

## Instructions

- Use black ink or black ball-point pen. Draw diagrams in pencil.
- Read each question carefully before you start to write your answer.
- Answer **all** questions in the spaces provided.
- Show your working in any calculator question and include units in your answer where appropriate.
- In questions marked with an asterisk (*), marks will be awarded for your ability to structure your answer logically, showing how the points that you make are related or follow on from each other where appropriate.

## Information

- The marks for each question are shown in brackets.
  *Use this as a guide to how much time to spend on each question.*
- The maximum mark for this paper is 100.
- Diagrams are not accurately drawn unless otherwise stated.

Name: ....................................................................................................................

**1** The periodic table lists all known elements.

**(a)** Which statement about the periodic table is correct?
Tick (✓) **one** box. [1]

Each row begins with elements with one outer electron. ☐

The columns are called periods. ☐

The elements are arranged in mass number order. ☐

The metallic elements are on the right. ☐

**(b)** Which of these statements about the elements in Group 0 is correct?
Tick (✓) **one** box. [1]

They are all liquids at room temperature. ☐

Their boiling points increase as you go down the group. ☐

They have very high melting points. ☐

Their molecules are made from pairs of atoms. ☐

**(c)** Element X is a solid with a low melting point. When it reacts it forms covalent bonds with other elements or it forms negative ions.

Put an X where you would expect to find element X on the periodic table. [1]

**2** **(a)** Which statement explains why group 1 elements are known as the alkali metals?
Tick (✓) **one** box. [1]

They are tested with an alkali to show they are reactive. ☐

They are in the first column in the periodic table. ☐

They all react strongly with alkalis. ☐

They make an alkali when reacted with water. ☐

**(b)** Sodium is below lithium in group 1 of the periodic table.

Explain why sodium reacts more vigorously with water than lithium. **[2]**

.......................................................................................................................................................................

.......................................................................................................................................................................

**3** **(a)** Which list of metals correctly shows the order of reactivity, starting with the most reactive and ending with the least reactive?
Tick (✓) **one** box. **[1]**

lithium, calcium, zinc, iron ☐

calcium, lithium, iron, copper ☐

potassium, iron, zinc, copper ☐

magnesium, copper, lithium, zinc ☐

**(b)** Which of these properties applies only to transition metals?
Tick (✓) **one** box. **[1]**

Easily hammered into shape ☐

Conduct heat ☐

Form coloured compounds ☐

Good conductor of electricity ☐

**(c)** Steel is an alloy composed mainly of iron.

Explain why steel is a more useful metal than iron. **[2]**

.......................................................................................................................................................................

.......................................................................................................................................................................

*(d)** **Figure 1** shows the arrangement of particles in a metal.

**Figure 1**

| | |
|---|---|
| ............................... → | ⊕ ⊕ ⊕ ⊕ |
| ............................... → | ⊕ ⊕ ⊕ ⊕ |
| | ⊕ ⊕ ⊕ ⊕ |

Add labels to **Figure 1** and use them to explain how metals conduct electricity. **[4]**

.......................................................................................................................................................................

.......................................................................................................................................................................

**4** **(a)** Graphite is commonly used as a lubricant in machines that operate at high temperatures.

Which properties of graphite explain why it is suitable for this use?
Tick (✓) **one** box. [1]

Electrical conductor and high melting point ☐

Good heat and electrical conductor ☐

Good heat conductor and slippery ☐

High melting point and slippery ☐

**(b)** Graphene is a form of carbon. It is formed of a sheet of carbon atoms, one atom thick.

A graphene sheet has a thickness of $3.4 \times 10^{-8}$ cm. Calculate the area covered by 1 cm³ of graphene.
Tick (✓) **one** box. [1]

$3.4 \times 10^8$ cm² ☐

$2.9 \times 10^7$ cm² ☐

$2.9 \times 10^{-7}$ cm² ☐

$3.4 \times 10^{-8}$ cm² ☐

**(c)** Carbon nanotubes are cylindrical fullerenes.

Outline two important physical properties of nanotubes. [2]

......................................................................................................................................................

......................................................................................................................................................

**(d)** Diamond has a tetrahedral structure, as shown in **Figure 2**.

**Figure 2**

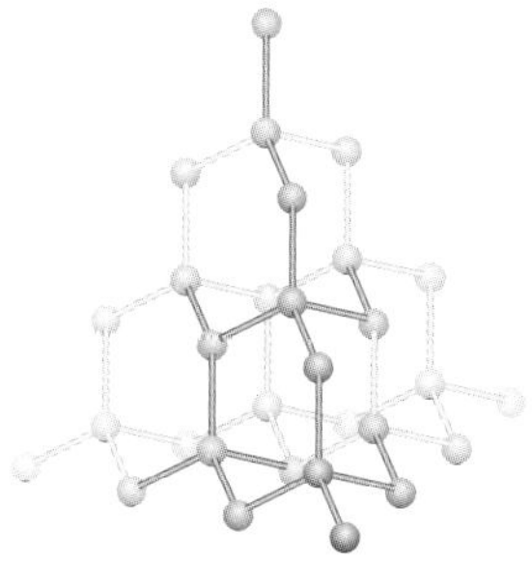

Explain why diamond has a very high melting point and why, unlike graphite, it does not conduct electricity. [3]

......................................................................................................................................................

......................................................................................................................................................

......................................................................................................................................................

**5** **(a)** Carbon dioxide is made by the thermal decomposition of copper(II) carbonate (see **Figure 3**). Copper(II) oxide is also made.

**Figure 3**

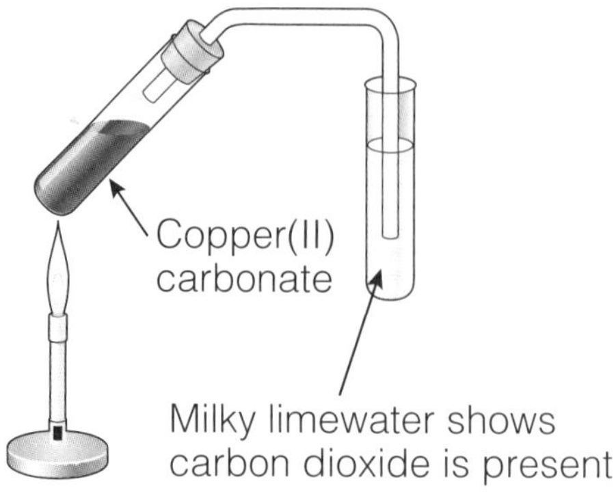

Copper(II) carbonate

Milky limewater shows carbon dioxide is present

Write the word equation for the decomposition reaction. **[1]**

..................................................................................................................................................

**(b)** Calculate the mass of carbon dioxide made when 12.35 g of copper(II) carbonate is heated to make 7.95 g of copper(II) oxide. Show your working. **[2]**

..................................................................................................................................................

..................................................................................................................................................

**6** **(a)** Draw a diagram to show the arrangement of electrons in a magnesium atom. **[1]**

**(b)** Magnesium (Mg) burns in oxygen ($O_2$) to make magnesium oxide (MgO).

**(i)** Balance the formula equation for this reaction. **[1]**

$$[............]Mg + [............]O_2 \rightarrow [............]MgO$$

**(ii)** The reaction to make magnesium oxide has a 100% atom economy. How can you tell from the equation? **[1]**

..................................................................................................................................................

**(iii)** Draw a dot-and-cross diagram to show the bonding in magnesium oxide. **[2]**

**(c)** Ria made 9.6 g of magnesium chloride by reacting magnesium oxide with hydrochloric acid:

$$MgO + 2HCl \rightarrow MgCl_2 + H_2O$$

She calculated that from the amounts she used, she should have made 12.8 g.

Calculate the percentage yield of magnesium chloride. Show your working. **[2]**

.......................................................................................................................................................

.......................................................................................................................................................

...........................................%

**7** **(a)** Which of these statements about a neutral atom is always correct?
Tick (✓) **one** box. **[1]**

It has the same number of electrons and neutrons. ☐

It has the same number of protons and neutrons. ☐

It has the same number of protons, neutrons and electrons. ☐

It has the same number of electrons and protons. ☐

**(b) (i)** $Fe^{2+}$ ions are formed during some chemical reactions. Look at the information given below and then complete **Table 1**. **[1]**

$$^{54}_{26}Fe^{2+}$$

Table 1

| Number of protons in the ion | |
|---|---|
| Number of neutrons in the ion | |
| Number of electrons in the ion | |

**\*(ii)** Explain how you worked out each of the three numbers. **[3]**

**Number of protons:**

.......................................................................................................................................................

.......................................................................................................................................................

**Number of neutrons:**

.......................................................................................................................................................

.......................................................................................................................................................

**Number of electrons:**

.......................................................................................................................................................

.......................................................................................................................................................

**8** The element chlorine has two naturally occurring isotopes.

What are the similarities and differences in the atomic structure of the two isotopes? **[3]**

...................................................................................................................................................................

...................................................................................................................................................................

...................................................................................................................................................................

**9** Gold metal can be rolled into very thin sheets called gold leaf.

The radius of a gold atom is $1.5 \times 10^{-10}$ m.

Gold leaf has a typical thickness of $1.2 \times 10^{-6}$ m.

Calculate how many gold atoms are packed on top of each other to achieve this thickness. **[2]**

...................................................................................................................................................................

...................................................................................................................................................................

...................................................................................................................................................................

**10** **(a)** Acids react with bases to form salts and water. Which pair of reactants can be used to prepare copper sulfate?
Tick (✓) **one** box. **[1]**

Copper and sulfuric acid ☐

Copper hydroxide and nitric acid ☐

Copper oxide and sulfuric acid ☐

Copper oxide and hydrochloric acid ☐

**(b)** Josh put a sample of potassium hydroxide solution into a beaker. He measured the pH. Then he slowly added dilute nitric acid until no further reaction took place.

How would the pH of the solution in the beaker change?
Tick (✓) **one** box. **[1]**

The pH would start high and decrease to below 7. ☐

The solution would change to a pH of 7. ☐

The pH would stay the same. ☐

The pH would start low and increase to above 7. ☐

(c) Which of the following 0.1 mol/dm³ acid solutions has the lowest pH?
    Tick (✓) **one** box. [1]

Carbonic acid ☐

Citric acid ☐

Ethanoic acid ☐

Nitric acid ☐

(d) (i) An acid–base reaction was completed between hydrochloric acid (HCl) and calcium oxide
    (CaO) to make calcium chloride ($CaCl_2$).

    This is the equation for the reaction: $2HCl + CaO \rightarrow CaCl_2 + H_2O$

    An excess of solid calcium oxide was added to the acid.

    Calculate the minimum mass of calcium oxide needed to make 5.55 g of calcium chloride.
    Show your working. [4]

    ...........................................................................................................................................................

    ...........................................................................................................................................................

    ...........................................................................................................................................................

    ...........................................................................................................................................................

(ii) Lithium nitrate can be made using a similar method, by reacting solid lithium carbonate with
     nitric acid.

     This is the equation for the reaction: $Li_2CO_3 + 2HNO_3 \rightarrow 2LiNO_3 + CO_2 + H_2O$

     Relative formula masses: $Li_2CO_3 = 74$; $HNO_3 = 63$; $LiNO_3 = 69$

     Use the equation to calculate the percentage atom economy for making lithium nitrate from
     lithium carbonate. [3]

     $$\frac{\text{relative formula mass of desired product from equation}}{\text{sum of relative formula masses of all reactants from equation}} \times 100$$

     ...........................................................................................................................................................

     ...........................................................................................................................................................

     ...........................................................................................................................................................

**11** Copper(II) sulfate solution can undergo electrolysis using the apparatus shown in **Figure 4**.

**Figure 4**

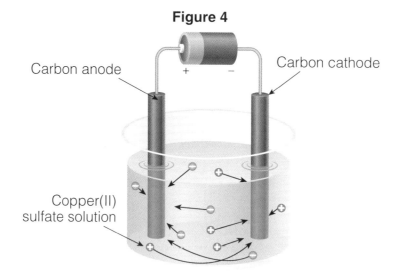

Carbon anode

Carbon cathode

Copper(II) sulfate solution

**(a)** Describe the meaning of the term electrolysis. **[2]**

..................................................................................................................................................

..................................................................................................................................................

*__(b)__ These are the reactions at the electrodes during the electrolysis of copper(II) sulfate solution:

Cathode $\qquad$ $Cu^{2+} + 2e^- \rightarrow Cu$

Anode $\qquad$ $4OH^- \rightarrow O_2 + 2H_2O + 4e^-$

Which reaction is reduction and which reaction is oxidation? Explain your answer. **[2]**

..................................................................................................................................................

..................................................................................................................................................

..................................................................................................................................................

**12** Iron(III) oxide is roasted with carbon (coke) in a blast furnace to produce iron. In one of the reactions in the furnace, carbon reacts with oxygen in the air to make carbon monoxide.

Carbon monoxide (CO) then reacts with the iron(III) oxide ($Fe_2O_3$) to make iron (Fe). The other product is carbon dioxide.

**(a)** Write a balanced symbol equation for the reaction of carbon monoxide with iron(III) oxide. **[2]**

..................................................................................................................................................

**(b)** Heating a metal oxide with carbon is a common method used to extract the metal.

Explain why copper can be extracted from copper oxide but aluminium cannot be extracted from its oxide by this method. **[2]**

..................................................................................................................................................

..................................................................................................................................................

**(c)** Aluminium is extracted by the electrolysis of molten aluminium oxide ($Al_2O_3$).

Write the ionic half equation for the reaction at each electrode. **[2]**

**Cathode:** ..................................................................................

**Anode:** ..................................................................................

**13** **(a)** Hydrogen fuel cells can be used to make electricity: $2H_2 + O_2 \rightarrow 2H_2O$

Give two advantages of using hydrogen fuel cells rather than using batteries. **[2]**

..............................................................................................................................................................

..............................................................................................................................................................

**(b) (i)** Hydrogen gas is converted into hydrogen ions at the anode in the fuel cell.

Write an ionic half equation to show how hydrogen ions are made at the anode. **[1]**

..........................................................................................

**(ii)** Oxygen gas is converted into oxide ions at the cathode in the fuel cell.

Write an ionic half equation to show how oxide ions are made at the cathode. **[1]**

..........................................................................................

**(c)** Complete the energy level diagram for the hydrogen fuel cell (see **Figure 5**). Mark on **Figure 5** the activation energy for the reaction. **[3]**

**Figure 5**

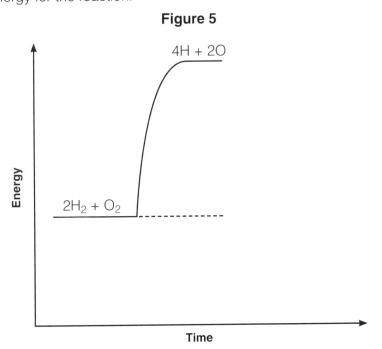

**14** Ella measured 15 cm³ of water into a test tube, as shown in **Figure 6**.

**Figure 6**

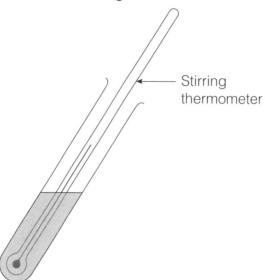

Stirring
thermometer

She measured the temperature of the water and added 2 g of a solid. She stirred until there was no further temperature change. She repeated the experiment with other solids.

**(a)** Complete the results table (**Table 2**). [2]

**Table 2**

| Solid | Start temperature (°C) | End temperature (°C) | Temperature change (°C) |
|---|---|---|---|
| Ammonium chloride | 15 | 9 | −6 |
| Potassium hydroxide | 16 | 29 | +13 |
| Ammonium nitrate | 18 | 4 | .......... |
| Sodium hydroxide | 17 | 35 | .......... |

**\*(b)** Which of the solids had the largest endothermic energy change? Explain your answer. [3]

................................................................................................................................................

................................................................................................................................................

................................................................................................................................................

**15** **(a)** Oxygen has a boiling point of −183°C and a melting point of −219°C.

Describe what happens to the arrangement and movement of oxygen molecules as the temperature is changed from −190°C to −170°C. [2]

................................................................................................................................................

................................................................................................................................................

................................................................................................................................................

**(b)** A small, portable oxygen cylinder for medical use (like **Figure 7**) contains 15 000 g of liquid oxygen.

**Figure 7**

The $M_r$ of oxygen ($O_2$) is 32. One mole of any gas at room temperature and pressure has a volume of 24 dm³.

What volume of oxygen gas in dm³ will this cylinder provide at room temperature and pressure? Show your working. **[2]**

.................................................................................................................................................................

.................................................................................................................................................................

\* **16** Our understanding of the model of the atom has developed from the work of a number of scientists, starting from Dalton's theory that an atom was a solid sphere.

Outline how our understanding of the atom has changed. Link the key scientists with the improvements they made to our understanding. **[6]**

.................................................................................................................................................................

.................................................................................................................................................................

.................................................................................................................................................................

.................................................................................................................................................................

.................................................................................................................................................................

.................................................................................................................................................................

.................................................................................................................................................................

.................................................................................................................................................................

.................................................................................................................................................................

.................................................................................................................................................................

*17 (a) Finlay added an aqueous solution of sodium iodide to a solution of bromine. The colour changed from orange to deep brown.

Finlay then added an aqueous solution of sodium chloride to the bromine solution. The orange colour did not change.

Explain these observations. [4]

.......................................................................................................................................

.......................................................................................................................................

.......................................................................................................................................

.......................................................................................................................................

(b) Chlorine is composed of diatomic molecules, $Cl_2$.

Draw a dot-and-cross diagram to show the bonding in a chlorine molecule. You should only show the outer shell electrons in your diagram. [2]

(c) Chlorine and iodine are both in group 7 of the periodic table.

Explain why chlorine is a gas and iodine is a solid at room temperature. [2]

.......................................................................................................................................

.......................................................................................................................................

(d) Explain why solid iodine does not conduct electricity. [1]

.......................................................................................................................................

18 (a) When 1 mole of carbon burns completely, 393 kJ of energy is released.

$$C_{(s)} + O_{2(g)} \rightarrow CO_{2(g)}$$

The relative atomic mass ($A_r$) of carbon = 12.

Calculate the energy released when 14.4 g of carbon is burned. Show your working. [2]

.......................................................................................................................................

.......................................................................................................................................

.......................................................................................................................................

*(b) Energy is released when carbon burns. Use ideas about bond making and bond breaking to explain why. [3]

...........................................................................................................................................

...........................................................................................................................................

...........................................................................................................................................

...........................................................................................................................................

(c) Amy measured the energy released by reacting hydrochloric acid with sodium hydroxide solution. Both solutions had the same concentration.

This was the method used.

**1** Measure 25 cm³ sodium hydroxide solution using a 100 cm³ measuring cylinder.

**2** Pour the sodium hydroxide solution into a 250 cm³ beaker.

**3** Use the 100 cm³ measuring cylinder to measure 25 cm³ hydrochloric acid.

**4** Pour the acid into the sodium hydroxide in the beaker.

**5** Measure the start temperature with a thermometer.

**6** After one minute, measure the final temperature.

This method gave a poor result. Suggest three improvements to the method. [3]

**1:** .....................................................................................................................................

...........................................................................................................................................

**2:** .....................................................................................................................................

...........................................................................................................................................

**3:** .....................................................................................................................................

...........................................................................................................................................

**TOTAL FOR PAPER = 100 MARKS**

# GCSE (9–1)
# Chemistry
**Paper 2**

## Higher tier
Time: 1 hour 45 minutes

**You may use:**

- a calculator
- a ruler
- a periodic table.

## Instructions

- Use black ink or black ball-point pen. Draw diagrams in pencil.
- Read each question carefully before you start to write your answer.
- Answer **all** questions in the spaces provided.
- Show your working in any calculator question and include units in your answer where appropriate.
- In questions marked with an asterisk (*), marks will be awarded for your ability to structure your answer logically, showing how the points that you make are related or follow on from each other where appropriate.

## Information

- The marks for each question are shown in brackets.
  *Use this as a guide to how much time to spend on each question.*
- The maximum mark for this paper is 100.
- Diagrams are not accurately drawn unless otherwise stated.

Name: ................................................................................................................

**1** **(a)** Which one of the following gases will bleach damp litmus paper?
Tick (✓) **one** box. [1]

Carbon dioxide ☐

Chlorine ☐

Hydrogen ☐

Methane ☐

**(b)** Which one of the following gases is a raw material for the Haber process?
Tick (✓) **one** box. [1]

Carbon dioxide ☐

Chlorine ☐

Hydrogen ☐

Methane ☐

**(c)** Which one of the following gases is made when ethanoic acid reacts with calcium carbonate?
Tick (✓) **one** box. [1]

Carbon dioxide ☐

Chlorine ☐

Hydrogen ☐

Methane ☐

**2** The apparatus used in the laboratory for cracking long-chain hydrocarbons is shown in **Figure 1**.

**Figure 1**

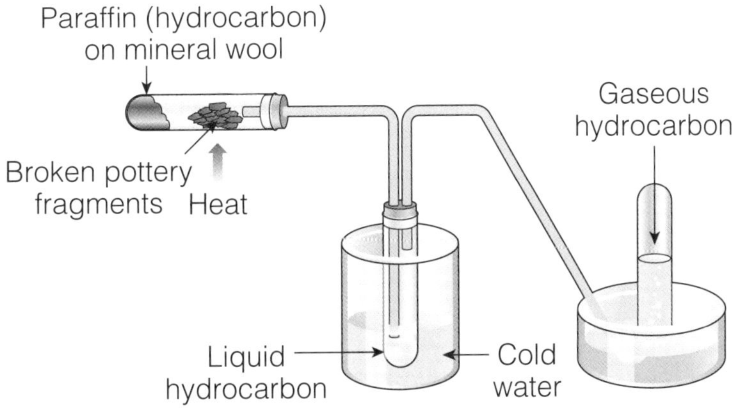

**(a)** Explain what is meant by **cracking** long-chain hydrocarbons. [2]

..................................................................................................................................................................

..................................................................................................................................................................

**(b)** What is the purpose of the broken pottery fragments? [1]

..................................................................................................................................................................

**(c)** The paraffin on the mineral wool has the formula $C_{16}H_{34}$. The gaseous product is ethene ($C_2H_4$) and the liquid hydrocarbon is decane ($C_{10}H_{22}$).

Construct a balanced symbol equation for the reaction. [2]

..................................................................................................................................................................

*3 Explain how the difference in strength of intermolecular forces between hydrocarbons allows them to be separated by fractional distillation. [3]

..................................................................................................................................................................

..................................................................................................................................................................

..................................................................................................................................................................

4 Which of the following hydrocarbons is the most flammable?
Tick (✓) **one** box. [1]

$C_8H_{18}$ ☐

$C_{11}H_{24}$ ☐

$C_5H_{12}$ ☐

$C_{14}H_{30}$ ☐

5 Five students each have a test tube containing $10\,cm^3$ of hydrochloric acid of the same concentration. They each have a different-sized strip of magnesium ribbon.

They drop the magnesium into the acid and time how long it takes for the fizzing to stop.

**Table 1** shows the results of the experiment.

**Table 1**

| Student | Iram | Alex | Dylan | Georgie | Noah |
|---|---|---|---|---|---|
| Time (s) | 246 | 258 | 204 | 300 | 272 |

**(a)** Which student had the fastest reaction? [1]

..................................................................................................................................................................

**(b)** Georgie noticed that there was some magnesium left in the test tube when the fizzing stopped. In all the other test tubes, there was no magnesium left. Explain these two observations. [2]

..................................................................................................................................................................

..................................................................................................................................................................

..................................................................................................................................................................

**(c) (i)** Georgie repeated her experiment.

This time she measured the volume of gas made with a gas syringe. She measured 94.5 cm³ of gas made in 225 seconds.

Calculate the mean rate of reaction. Show your working and include the unit in your answer. **[3]**

...................................................................................................................................................

...................................................................................................................................................

...................................................................................................................................................

**(ii)** Georgie repeated her experiment again. This time she used double the volume of acid and double the amount of magnesium.

Predict what happened to the amount of gas made in the reaction. Explain your answer. **[2]**

...................................................................................................................................................

...................................................................................................................................................

...................................................................................................................................................

**6** **Figure 2** shows the result of a chromatography experiment on an unknown black ink.

**Figure 2**

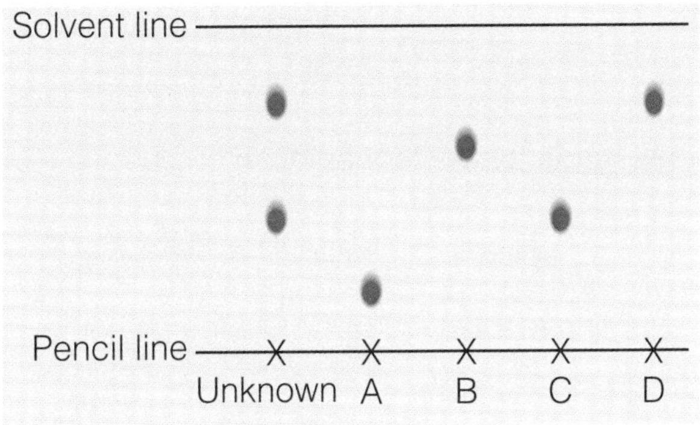

**(a)** Which inks does the unknown ink in **Figure 2** contain?
Tick (✓) **one** box. **[1]**

A and B ☐

A and C ☐

B and D ☐

C and D ☐

**(b)** The $R_f$ value of ink B is 0.86  The solvent line moved 7.91 cm from the pencil line.

Calculate how far ink B moved up the paper. Show your working. Give your answer to an appropriate number of significant figures. **[2]**

...................................................................................................................................................

...................................................................................................................................................

**7** Which of the following formulations could be used as an NPK fertiliser?
Tick (✓) **one** box. [1]

Ammonium nitrate and sodium chloride ☐

Ammonium phosphate and potassium chloride ☐

Potassium chloride and potassium nitrate ☐

Potassium sulfate and sodium nitrate ☐

**8** **(a)** Which of the following molecules has the formula $C_4H_{10}$? Tick (✓) **one** box. [1]

**(b)** Write the balanced symbol equation for the complete combustion of $C_4H_{10}$. [2]

...............................................................................................................................................................

**9** Ethanol ($C_2H_5OH$) is an alcohol made by the fermentation of glucose ($C_6H_{12}O_6$):

$$C_6H_{12}O_6 \rightarrow 2C_2H_5OH + 2CO_2$$

**(a)** The optimum temperature for this reaction is 35°C. Outline two other conditions for the reaction. [2]

...............................................................................................................................................................

...............................................................................................................................................................

***(b)** Explain why the yield of ethanol reduces if the temperature is above 35°C. [2]

...............................................................................................................................................................

...............................................................................................................................................................

**(c)** In some parts of the world, ethanol is mixed with petrol to make a fuel for cars. Outline one
advantage and one disadvantage of using ethanol from fermentation as a fuel. [2]

...............................................................................................................................................................

...............................................................................................................................................................

**(d)** What is the name of the ester made when ethanol reacts with ethanoic acid in the presence of
concentrated sulfuric acid? [1]

...............................................................................................................................................................

**10** Which word best describes fibreglass?

Tick (✓) **one** box. **[1]**

Alloy ☐

Ceramic ☐

Composite ☐

Polymer ☐

**11** A nine carat wedding ring weighs 4.5 g. What is the weight of pure gold in the ring?

Pure gold is 24 carat.

Tick (✓) **one** box. **[1]**

0.50 g ☐

0.90 g ☐

1.69 g ☐

4.05 g ☐

**12 (a)** These statements describe the process by which the Earth's atmosphere has changed.

**A** Oceans formed as the temperature at the surface fell below 100°C.

**B** Photosynthesis released oxygen into the atmosphere and used up carbon dioxide.

**C** Nitrifying bacteria used up ammonia and released nitrogen.

**D** Hot volcanic earth released carbon dioxide and ammonia into the atmosphere.

Put each letter in the correct box to show the order that scientists now believe the atmosphere developed. **[2]**

☐ → ☐ → ☐ → ☐

**(b)** How the Earth's atmosphere evolved is a theory. What is a theory? **[2]**

...................................................................................................................................................

...................................................................................................................................................

**(c)** Explain why the way that the Earth's atmosphere evolved can only be a theory. **[1]**

...................................................................................................................................................

...................................................................................................................................................

**(d)** Which pie chart shows the composition of the Earth's atmosphere today? Tick (✓) **one** box. **[1]**

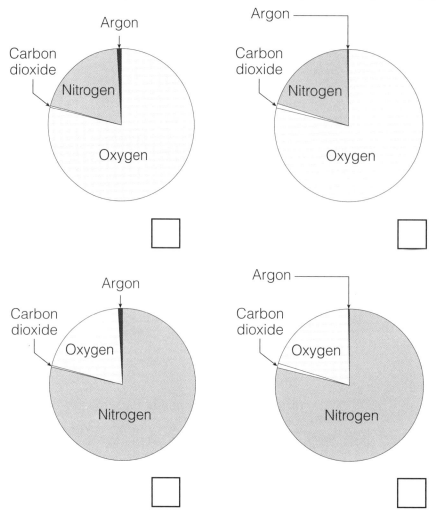

☐

☐

☐

☐

13  Meg carried out a rate of reaction experiment by reacting hydrochloric acid with sodium thiosulfate solution. A yellow precipitate of sulfur formed.

As shown in **Figure 3**, the reaction was followed by timing how long it took a cross drawn under a flask to disappear.

**Figure 3**

All reactions were carried out at 25°C. **Table 2** shows the results.

**Table 2**

| Concentration of acid (mol/dm³) | Time taken for cross to disappear (s) |
|---|---|
| 0.1 | 60 |
| 0.2 | 40 |
| 0.4 | 24 |
| 0.6 | 13 |
| 0.8 | 8 |
| 1.0 | 4 |

**(a)** Plot the results on the graph paper in **Figure 4**. [3]

**Figure 4**

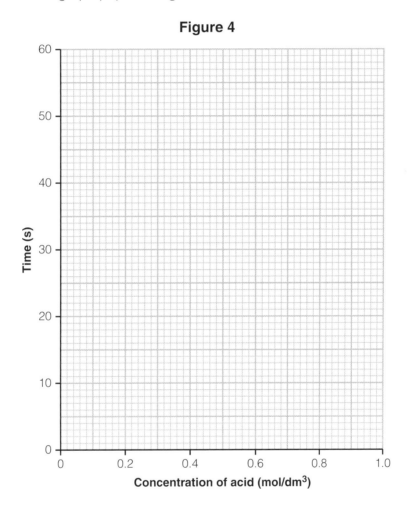

Concentration of acid (mol/dm³)

***(b)** Describe and explain how the rate of reaction changes as the concentration of acid changes. [3]

..............................................................................................................................................................

..............................................................................................................................................................

..............................................................................................................................................................

**(c)** The experiment was repeated at 35°C. Predict how the reaction times would change. [1]

..............................................................................................................................................................

**14** Explain the purpose of desalination and chlorination in making safe drinking water. **[2]**

**Desalination:**

..................................................................................................................................................

..................................................................................................................................................

**Chlorination:**

..................................................................................................................................................

..................................................................................................................................................

**15** The local water authority tested some river water.

The river was near a copper mine and it was suspected that the water was contaminated with copper(II) ions, $Cu^{2+}$, and sulfate ions, $SO_4^{2-}$.

**Table 3** shows the results of the tests on the river water.

**Table 3**

| Test | Result |
|---|---|
| Flame test | Crimson flame |
| Silver nitrate solution | Cream precipitate |
| Barium chloride solution | White precipitate |
| Sodium hydroxide solution | Brown precipitate |

**\*(a)** Describe how to carry out a flame test. Explain what the results of the four tests mean and decide whether they support the idea that the river water contains copper(II) and sulfate ions. **[6]**

..................................................................................................................................................

..................................................................................................................................................

..................................................................................................................................................

..................................................................................................................................................

..................................................................................................................................................

..................................................................................................................................................

..................................................................................................................................................

..................................................................................................................................................

..................................................................................................................................................

**(b)** The water sample was then analysed using flame emission spectroscopy. What extra information would this provide? **[2]**

..................................................................................................................................................

..................................................................................................................................................

**16** **Figure 5** shows how the yield of the Haber process changes with different conditions.

**Figure 5**

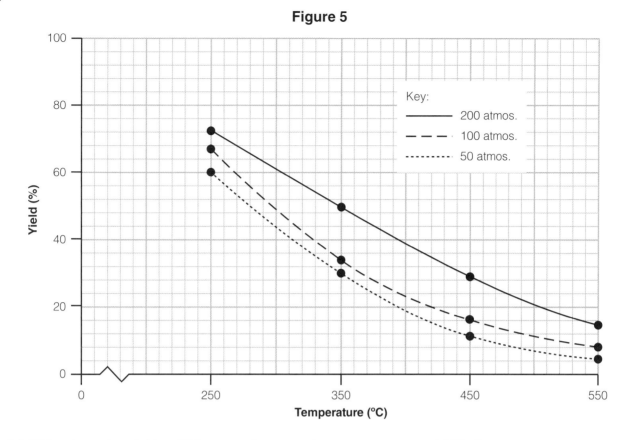

**(a)** Write down the yield at 200 atmospheres and at a temperature of 350°C. **[1]**

...........................................

**(b)** Describe what happens to the yield as the temperature is increased. **[1]**

......................................................................................................................................................

**(c)** This is the equation for the reaction: $N_{2(g)} + 3H_{2(g)} \rightleftharpoons 2NH_{3(g)}$

Use the equation to explain why the yield increases with increased pressure. **[2]**

......................................................................................................................................................

......................................................................................................................................................

......................................................................................................................................................

**(d)** Very high yields of ammonia can be achieved at a pressure of 500 atmospheres.

Explain why the normal operating pressure for the Haber process is much lower. **[2]**

......................................................................................................................................................

......................................................................................................................................................

......................................................................................................................................................

**17** **Figure 6** shows the results of an investigation into the reaction of zinc metal with hydrochloric acid.

Experiments A and B used 2 g of zinc: one experiment used zinc powder and the other used zinc granules.

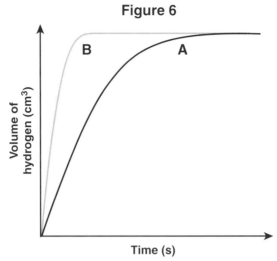

Figure 6

*(a)** Which line on the graph represents the reaction with powdered zinc?
Explain your answer using the idea of reacting particles. **[4]**

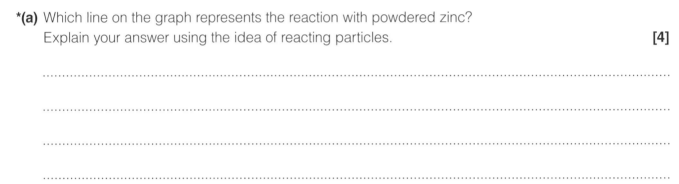

**(b)** Copper ions ($Cu^{2+}$) act as a catalyst for the reaction.

**Figure 7** shows the reaction profile without a catalyst.

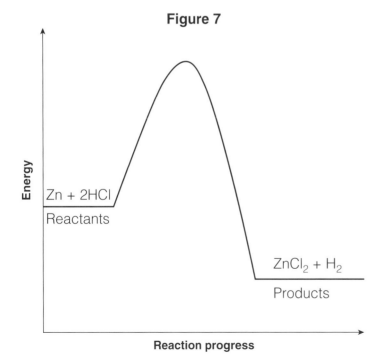

Figure 7

Draw on the graph the reaction profile with the catalyst. **[1]**

*18 **Table 4** shows some metals and their alloys.

**Table 4**

| | Order of hardness | Density (g/cm³) | Melting point (°C) | Order of strength |
|---|---|---|---|---|
| Copper | 5 | 8.9 | 1083 | 5 |
| Brass (alloy of copper) | 3 | 8.6 | 920 | 3 |
| Iron | 2 | 7.9 | 1538 | 2 |
| Steel (alloy of iron) | 1 | 7.8 | 1420 | 1 |
| Lead | 6 | 11.3 | 327 | 6 |
| Solder (alloy of lead) | 5 | 9.6 | 170 | 4 |

Use the data in the table to outline what alloying does to the properties of pure metals. **[4]**

..............................................................................................................................................................

..............................................................................................................................................................

..............................................................................................................................................................

..............................................................................................................................................................

19 The corrosion of iron can be prevented by coating it with a layer of zinc. This is called galvanising.

Explain how galvanising protects the iron from rusting. **[2]**

..............................................................................................................................................................

..............................................................................................................................................................

20 (a) Look at the displayed formula of propene in **Figure 8**.

**Figure 8**

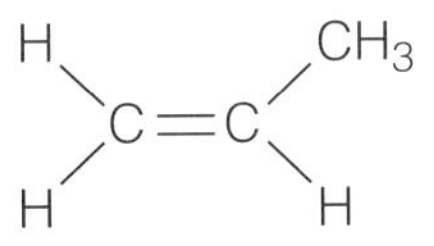

Propene molecules can join together to form the addition polymer, poly(propene).

Draw a diagram to show the structure of the polymer. **[3]**

**(b) Figure 9** shows the packing of some polymer molecules.

**Figure 9**

 Polymer A

 Polymer B

 Polymer C

 Polymer D

(i) Polymers A, C and D are thermosoftening polymers. Describe how the polymer chains behave when they are gently heated up. **[2]**

.................................................................................................................................................

.................................................................................................................................................

(ii) Explain why polymer B is **not** a thermosoftening polymer. **[2]**

.................................................................................................................................................

.................................................................................................................................................

(iii) Polymers A and D are both poly(ethene). Explain what caused the structures of the chains to be different. **[2]**

.................................................................................................................................................

.................................................................................................................................................

21 Sulfuric acid is manufactured in the contact process.

In one of the reactions in the process, sulfur dioxide is converted to sulfur trioxide:

$$2SO_{2(g)} + O_{2(g)} \rightleftharpoons 2SO_{3(g)}$$

This is a reversible reaction and will reach a position of equilibrium.

**(a)** Describe how the reaction reaches equilibrium from the start. Use ideas about rate of reaction. **[2]**

.................................................................................................................................................

.................................................................................................................................................

**(b)** Predict and explain the effect of reducing the pressure on the position of equilibrium for this reaction. **[2]**

..................................................................................................................................................

..................................................................................................................................................

**(c)** What is the effect of using a catalyst on the position of equilibrium in this reaction? **[1]**

..................................................................................................................................................

**(d)** Outline the extra information you need to determine the effect on the equilibrium position of increasing the temperature of the reaction mixture. **[1]**

..................................................................................................................................................

22 PET is a polymer that is used to manufacture water bottles (see **Figure 10**). PET is a polyester. The monomers that make PET contain two functional groups.

**Figure 10**

**(a)** Which two functional groups are needed to form a polyester? **[2]**

..................................................................................................................................................

..................................................................................................................................................

**(b)** Explain why the reaction that forms PET is called a condensation reaction. **[1]**

..................................................................................................................................................

**(c)** In a recent life-cycle assessment, the energy use for 1 kg of PET was 120 000 kJ. The assessment included an estimate for the energy use in transport of 14 000 kJ.

Explain why the transport energy use is an estimate. **[1]**

..................................................................................................................................................

**23** Catalytic converters are fitted to modern cars to reduce carbon monoxide and nitrogen dioxide emissions formed during the combustion of fuel (see **Figure 11**).

**Figure 11**

*(a) Describe how nitrogen dioxide gas is formed by the car. [3]

..........................................................................................................................................

..........................................................................................................................................

..........................................................................................................................................

(b) Sulfur dioxide can also be formed from burning fuels such as petrol or diesel. Catalytic converters cannot reduce sulfur dioxide emissions.

(i) Give one reason why sulfur dioxide is an atmospheric pollutant. [1]

..........................................................................................................................................

(ii) Suggest how emissions of sulfur dioxide can be reduced from cars that use diesel and petrol. [1]

..........................................................................................................................................

**TOTAL FOR PAPER = 100 MARKS**

# Answers

## Page 4
1. (a) Na **(1)** Cl **(1)**
   (b) Sodium + chlorine ⟶ sodium chloride **(reactants 1, products 1)**
   (c) A compound **(1)** as the elements are chemically combined/joined **(1)**
   (d) A mixture **(1)** as the salt and water are together but not chemically combined **(1)**
   (e) Crystallisation **(1)**; simple distillation **(1)**

## Page 5
1. (a) The plum pudding model proposed that an atom was a ball of positive charge/today's model has the positive charge contained in the nucleus/protons **(1)** The plum pudding model proposed that electrons were embedded/spread throughout the positive charge/today's model has the electrons in different energy levels/shells surrounding the positive charge **(1)**
   (b) Some of the positively charged particles/alpha particles (when fired at gold foil) were deflected **(1)**
   (c) Niels Bohr suggested that electrons orbit the nucleus at specific distances/are present in energy levels/shells **(1)** His calculations were backed up by experimental results **(1)**
   (d)

| Particle | Relative charge | Relative mass |
|----------|-----------------|---------------|
| Proton | +1 | 1 |
| Neutron | 0 | 1 |
| Electron | −1 | Negligible/approx. 1/2000 |

**(4)**

   (e) (i) 11 **(1)**
       (ii) 23 **(1)**

## Page 6
1. (a) 3 **(1)**
   (b) 2,7 **(1)**
   (c) 7 **(1)** As an atom of fluorine has 7 electrons in its outer shell **(1)**
2. (a) By increasing atomic number **(1)**
   (b) Because they both have similar chemical properties **(1)**
   (c) **Accept two from:** have high melting/boiling points; conduct heat and electricity; react with oxygen to form alkalis; malleable/ductile **(2)**

## Page 7
1. (a) The atoms have full outer shells/energy levels **(1)** so they do not bond **(1)**
   (b) It increases **(1)**
2. (a) $2Na_{(s)} + 2H_2O_{(l)} \longrightarrow 2NaOH_{(aq)} + H_{2(g)}$ **(1 for correct formula; 1 for correct balancing in equation. Ignore state symbols, even if wrong)**
   (b) Blue **(1)** as an alkali solution/the hydroxide ion is formed **(1)**
   (c) A potassium atom is larger (than a sodium atom), so the outer electron is further away from the nucleus **(1)** so there is less attraction/the electron is more easily lost **(1)**
3. (a) $2Na_{(s)} + Cl_{(g)} \longrightarrow 2NaCl_{(s)}$ **(1 for each side; any correctly balanced equation scores both marks, e.g. $4Na + 2Br_2 \longrightarrow 4NaBr$)**
   (b) Ionic **(1)**
   (c) chlorine + sodium bromide ⟶ sodium chloride **(1)** + bromine **(1)**
   (d) Displacement **(1)** A more reactive element (chlorine) takes the place of a less reactive element (bromine) in a compound **(1)**

## Page 8
1. (a) Metal M **(1)** as it is denser and has a higher melting point than metal L **(1)**
   (b) less **(1)**
   (c) Mercury **(1)**
2. (a) They form coloured compounds **(1)**
   (b) The iron is a catalyst **(1)** It speeds up the reaction/reduces the time taken for equilibrium to be reached **(1)**

## Page 9
1. sodium – metallic **(1)**; chlorine – simple molecular **(1)**; sodium chloride – ionic **(1)**
2. (a)

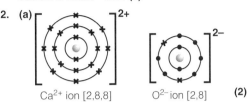

   $Ca^{2+}$ ion [2,8,8]     $O^{2-}$ ion [2,8]   **(2)**

   (b) Calcium: 2+, oxygen: 2– **(2)**
3. (a)

**(1)**

   (b) 2 **(1)**

## Page 10
1. (a) Electrostatic forces **(1)** between the anions and cations
   (b) CaO **(1)** There are an equal number of calcium ions and oxygen ions and so the ratio of each is 1:1 **(1)**
2. (a) A polymer **(1)**
   (b) $CH_2$ **(1)** There are twice as many hydrogen atoms as carbon atoms, so ratio of carbon to hydrogen is 1:2 **(1)**
3. Giant covalent/macromolecular **(1)** it is a large molecule consisting of atoms that are covalently bonded together with a theoretically infinite structure **(1)**

## Page 11
1. (a)

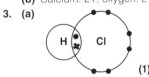

**(1 for regular arrangement of particles, 1 for no gaps between the particles)**

   (b) Intermolecular forces/forces between particles **(1)**
2. (a) It conducts electricity when liquid but not as a solid **(1)**
   (b) The ions **(1)** are not free to move **(1)**
   (c) Giant covalent/macromolecular **(1)** It has a high melting point <u>and</u> does not conduct electricity **(1)**
   (d) There are no free **(1)** charged particles/electrons/ions **(1)**

## Page 12
1. (a) The layers **(1)** (of ions) are able to slide over each other **(1)**
   (b) There is a strong attraction **(1)** between the metal cations and the delocalised electrons **(1)**
   (c) The electrons **(1)** are free to move/flow through the structure **(1)**
2. (a) A mixture of metals/a metal mixed with another element **(1)**
   (b) The layers are not able to slide over each other **(1)** because the other atoms are larger and prevent movement **(1)**
3. (a) **Accept two from:** for drug delivery into the body/as lubricants/reinforcing materials, e.g. in tennis rackets **(2)**
   (b) **Accept two from:** tensile strength; electrical conductivity; thermal conductivity **(2)**
   (c) A carbon nanotube is a cylindrical fullerene **(1)**

## Page 13
1. Coarse particles/dust ($PM_{10}$) – Between $1 \times 10^{-5}$ and $2.5 \times 10^{-6}$ m **(1)**; Fine particles ($PM_{2.5}$) – Between $1 \times 10^{-7}$ and $2.5 \times 10^{-6}$ m **(1)** Nanoparticles – Less than $1 \times 10^{-7}$ m (100 nm) **(1)**
2. (a) Owing to their higher/different surface area to volume ratio **(1)**
   (b) That smaller quantities may be needed to be effective compared with materials with normal-sized particles **(1)**

3. (a) Decreasing particle size increases **(1)** the surface area to volume ratio (or converse argument: increasing particle size decreases **(1)** the surface area to volume ratio)
   (b) **Accept two from:** synthetic skin; controlled drug delivery; electronics; development of new catalysts for fuel-cell materials; in deodorants and fabrics to prevent the growth of bacteria **(2)**
   (c) Advantages: better skin coverage **(1)**; more effective protection from the Sun's ultraviolet rays **(1)**; Potential disadvantages: cell damage in the body **(1)**/harmful effects on the environment **(1)**

## Page 14

1. (a) Total mass of reactants = total mass of the products, i.e. there is no net mass loss or gain during a chemical reaction **(1)**
   (b)
   | Substance | $A_r$ / $M_r$ |
   |-----------|---------------|
   | Al | 27 |
   | $Fe_2O_3$ | 160 |
   | $Al_2O_3$ | 102 |
   | Fe | 56 |
   **(4)**

2. (a) Oxygen **(1)** is added **(1)** to the magnesium
   (b) $2Mg_{(s)} + O_{2(g)} \longrightarrow 2MgO_{(s)}$ **(1 for reactants and products, 1 for correct balancing)**
   (c) The magnesium carbonate loses/gives off **(1)** carbon dioxide **(1)**
   (d) $MgCO_{3(s)} \longrightarrow MgO_{(s)} + CO_{2(g)}$ **(1 for correct formulae products; 1 for balanced equation; ignore state symbols, even if wrong)**

## Page 15

1. (a) $2.408 \times 10^{24}$ ($4 \times 6.02 \times 10^{23}$) **(1)**
   (b) 92 g ($4 \times 23$ g) **(1)**
   (c) 0.5 ($11.5 \div 23$) **(1)**
   (d) 4 moles of Na form 2 moles of $Na_2O$ (2:1 ratio), therefore 0.5 mole of Na forms 0.25 mole of $Na_2O$ mass = $0.5 \times 62$ **(1 for correct $M_r$ of $Na_2O$)** = 31 g **(1)**

2. (a) $6 \div 12 = 0.5$, $1 \div 1 = 1$ **(1)**
   $0.5 \div 0.5 = 1$, $1 \div 0.5 = 2$ **(1)**
   Empirical formula = $CH_2$ **(1)**
   (b) (relative formula mass of empirical formula = 14), $98 \div 14 = 7$ **(1)**
   Molecular formula = $C_7H_{14}$ **(1)**

## Page 16

1. (a) $(11.5 \div 15) \times 100$ **(1)** = 76.7% (3 sig. fig.) **(1)**
   (b) (i) $7 \div 28$ **(1)** = 0.25 **(1)**
   (ii) 0.25 **(1)** due to the 1:1 ratio of moles of ethene to moles of ethanol **(1)**
   (iii) $0.5 \times 46$ **(1)** = 23 g **(1)**
   (iv) $(11 \div 23) \times 100$ **(1)** = 47.8% **(1)**
   (c) Fermentation method: $(92 \div 180) \times 100 = 51.1\%$ **(1)** ethene with steam method: $[(46 : (28 + 18)] \times 100 = 100\%$ **(1)**

## Page 17

1. (a) Pipette **(1)**
   (b) Burette **(1)**
   (c) The indicator will change colour **(1)**

2. (a) $(23.80 \times 0.2) \div 1000$ **(1)** = 0.00476 **(1)**
   (b) 0.00476 **(1)** due to the 1:1 mole ratio of LiOH to HCl **(1)**
   (c) $(0.00476 \times 1000) \div 25$ **(1)** = 0.19 mol/dm³ **(1)**
   (d) $0.19 \times 36.5$ **(1)** = 6.94 g/dm³ **or** 6.95 g/dm³ **(1)**
   (e) $(6.94 \div 1000) \times 25$ **(1)** = 0.17 g **(1)**

## Page 18

1. (a) $120 \div 24\,000$ (also accept $0.12 \div 24$) = 0.005 **(1)**
   (b) Moles of magnesium reacting = $6 \div 24 = 0.25$ **(1)**
   moles of oxygen reacting = $0.5 \times 0.25 = 0.125$ **(1)**
   volume of oxygen = $0.125 \times 24 = 3$ dm³ (or $0.125 \times 24\,000 = 3000$ cm³) **(1)**

2.
| Chemical | Pb | $O_2$ | PbO |
|----------|-----|-------|-----|
| Mass from question/g | 41.4 | 3.2 | 44.6 |
| $A_r$ or $M_r$ | 207 | 32 | 223 |
| Moles = $\dfrac{mass}{M_r}$ | $\dfrac{41.4}{207}$ = 0.2 | $\dfrac{3.2}{32}$ = 0.1 | $\dfrac{44.6}{223}$ = 0.2 |
| ÷ smallest | $\dfrac{0.2}{0.1}$ = 2 | $\dfrac{0.1}{0.1}$ = 1 | $\dfrac{0.2}{0.1}$ = 2 |

Balanced equation: $2Pb + O_2 \longrightarrow 2PbO$ **(1 for each row in table, 1 for correct balanced equation)**

## Page 19

1. (a) calcium + oxygen $\longrightarrow$ calcium oxide **(1 for reactants, 1 for product)**
   (b) Calcium gains **(1)** oxygen **(1)** (**Also accept** Oxygen **(1)** is added **(1)** or Calcium loses **(1)** electrons **(1)**))
   (c) Potassium, sodium or lithium (or any other metal in group 1 or strontium, barium or radium) **(1)** the metal is more reactive than calcium/is above calcium in the reactivity series **(1)**
   (d) Metal + calcium oxide $\longrightarrow$ metal oxide + calcium, e.g. potassium + calcium oxide $\longrightarrow$ potassium oxide + calcium **(1 for reactants, 1 for products)**
   (e) Calcium oxide **(1)**

2. (a) Electrolysis **(1)**
   (b) $2Fe_2O_3 + 3C \longrightarrow 4Fe + 3CO_2$ **(1 for correct formulae, 1 for balanced equation; allow any correct balanced equation, e.g. $4Fe_2O_3 + 6C \longrightarrow 8Fe + 6CO_2$ ignore state symbols)**
   (c) Reduction **(1)** as electrons are gained **(1)** by the $Al^{3+}$ **(1)**
   (d) K **(1)** as it loses electrons **(1)** $K \longrightarrow K^+ + e$ **(1)**

## Page 20

1. (a) Zinc sulfate **(1)**
   (b) Zinc oxide + hydrochloric acid $\longrightarrow$ zinc chloride **(1)** + water **(1)**
   (c) Carbon dioxide **(1)** $CO_2$ **(1)**
   (d) (i) calcium (as it loses electrons) **(1)**
   (ii) $H^+$ **(1; allow $2H^+$ not hydrogen)**
   (e) When a substance loses **(1)** electrons **(1)**

2. (a) **Accept three from:** measure out some sulfuric acid (e.g. 25 cm³ in a measuring cylinder); transfer to a beaker and warm the acid; add copper oxide, stir and repeat until no more copper oxide dissolves; filter the mixture; leave the filtrate somewhere warm/heat the filtrate **(3)**
   (b) Nitric acid **(1)**
   (c) Soluble salt **(1)**

## Page 21

1. (a) 1–6 **(1)**
   (b) Hydrogen ion **(1)** $H^+$ **(1)**
   (c) Hydrochloric acid **(1)**
   (d) $H^+_{(aq)} + OH^-_{(aq)} \longrightarrow H_2O_{(l)}$ **(1 for correct formulae, 1 for correct state symbols)**

2. (a) A strong acid completely ionises/fully dissociates in water **(1)** a weak acid partially ionises/dissociates in water **(1)**
   (b) $CH_3COOH_{(aq)} \rightleftharpoons CH_3COO^-_{(aq)} + H^+_{(aq)}$ **or** $CH_3COOH_{(aq)} + aq \rightleftharpoons CH_3COO^-_{(aq)} + H^+_{(aq)}/CH_3COOH_{(aq)} + H_2O_{(l)} \rightleftharpoons CH_3COO^-_{(aq)} + H_3O^+_{(aq)}$ **(1 for reactants, 1 for products; ignore state symbols)**
   (c) Lower **(1)** Nitric acid is a stronger acid and so there will be more $H^+$ ions than in a weak acid and therefore will be more acidic **(1)**
   (d) It increases **(1)** by 1 **(1)**

## Page 22

1. (a) Cations **(1)**
   (b) Anions **(1)**
   (c) So that the ions **(1)** are free to move **(1)**
   (d) Oxidation **(1)** as electrons are lost **(1)**

**2. (a)**

| Solution | Product at anode | Product at cathode |
|---|---|---|
| NaCl | $H_2$ | $Cl_2$ |
| $KNO_3$ | $H_2$ | $O_2$ |
| $CuSO_4$ | Cu | $O_2$ |
| Water diluted with sulfuric acid | $H_2$ | $O_2$ |

(6)

**(b)** Hydrogen is produced because hydrogen ions are present in the solution **(1)** and hydrogen is less reactive than sodium **(1)**

**(c)** $4OH^- \longrightarrow O_2 + 2H_2O + 4e^-$ (or $4OH^- - 4e^- \longrightarrow O_2 + 2H_2O$)
**(1 for reactants and products, 1 for balanced equation; ignore state symbols)**

**Page 23**

**1. (a)**

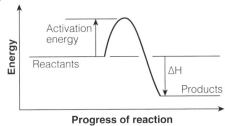

**(1 for products lower in energy than the reactants, each correct label scores 1)**

**(b)** More energy is released when the bonds in the product molecules are made **(1)** than is used to break the bonds in the reactant molecules **(1)**

**(c) Accept one from**: any thermal decomposition reaction (e.g. metal carbonate $\longrightarrow$ metal oxide + carbon dioxide); The reaction between citric acid and sodium hydrogencarbonate **(1)**

**2. (a)** $\Delta H$ = Bonds broken – bonds formed = 2144 **(1)** – 2348 **(1)** = –204 kJ/mol **(1)**

**(b)** Exothermic **(1)** the value of $\Delta H$ is negative/more energy is released when the bonds in the product molecules are made than is used to break the bonds in the reactant molecules **(1)**

**Page 24**

1. Two different metals **(1)** in contact with an electrolyte **(1)**
2. The metals are of different reactivity **(1)** and electrons flow from the more reactive metal to the less reactive metal **(1)**
3. Changing one or both of the metals **(1)** changing the electrolyte **(1)**
4. One of the reactants gets used up **(1)**
5. A fuel cell has a constant supply of fuel/in a chemical cell, all of the fuels are contained within the cell **(1)**
6. $2H_{2(g)} + O_{2(g)} \longrightarrow 2H_2O_{(l)}$ **(1 for reactants and products, 1 for balanced equation; ignore state symbols)**

**Page 25**

**1. (a)** 70°C **(1)**

**(b)** Increased temperature increases the rate of reaction **(1)** the higher the temperature, the more kinetic energy the particles have and so the frequency of collisions/successful collisions increases **(1)**

**2. (a)** 1st experiment: 69 ÷ 46 = 1.5 **(1)** cm³/s; 2nd experiment: 18 ÷ 10 = 1.8 **(1)** cm³/s **(1 for correct units)**

**(b)** The second experiment **(1)** as the rate is greater **(1)**

**Page 26**

**1. (a)** The particles must collide with enough energy/the activation energy **(1)**

**(b) (i)** At a higher concentration, there are more particles per unit volume/in the same volume of solution **(1)** meaning that there will be more collisions **(1)**

**(ii)** At a higher pressure there are more gas molecules per unit volume **(1)**, which means that there is an increased likelihood of a collision **(1)**

**(c)**

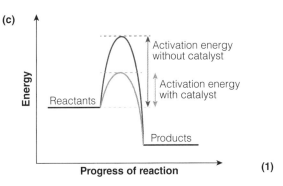

(1)

**(d)** Catalysts provide an alternative reaction pathway **(1)** of lower activation energy **(1)**

**Page 27**

**1. (a)** The blue crystals will turn white **(1)**

**(b)** hydrated copper(II) sulfate $\rightleftharpoons$ anhydrous copper(II) sulfate + water **(allow arrow $\longrightarrow$ instead of $\rightleftharpoons$) (1 for formulae, 1 for balanced equation)**

**(c)** The white powder will turn blue **(1)**

**(d)** Exothermic reaction **(1)**

**2. (a)** A reversible reaction **(1)**

**(b)** The yield of $SO_3$ would increase **(1)** higher pressure favours the reaction/shifts the equilibrium **(1)** to the side that produces fewer molecules of gas **(1)**

**(c)** The yield of $SO_3$ would decrease **(1)** increasing temperature favours the endothermic reaction **(1)**, which in this case is the reverse reaction **(1)**

**Page 28**

**1. (a)** Kerosene **(1)**

**(b)** It increases **(1)**

**(c)** 1. Crude oil is heated/boiled **(1)** 2. In the fractionating column there is a temperature gradient (hotter at bottom/cooler at top) **(1)** 3. The hydrocarbons travel up the fractionating column and condense at their boiling point **(1)**

**2. (a)** $C_nH_{2n+2}$ **(1)**

**(b)**

$$\begin{array}{c} \quad H \quad H \quad H \\ \quad | \quad\; | \quad\; | \\ H-C-C-C-H \\ \quad | \quad\; | \quad\; | \\ \quad H \quad H \quad H \end{array}$$ **(1)**

**(c)** $C_3H_{8(g)} + 5O_{2(g)} \longrightarrow 3CO_{2(g)} + 4H_2O_{(l)}$ **(1 for correct formulae, 1 for correct balancing; ignore state symbols)**

**Page 29**

**1. (a)** $C_nH_{2n}$ **(1)**

**(b)**

$$\begin{array}{c} H \quad\quad H \\ \backslash \quad\quad / \\ C=C \\ / \quad\quad \backslash \\ H \quad\quad H \end{array} \text{ or } \begin{array}{c} H \\ | \\ C=C-C-H \\ | \quad | \quad | \\ H \quad H \quad H \end{array} \text{ or } \begin{array}{c} H \quad H \quad H \\ | \quad | \quad | \\ H-C-C=C \\ | \quad | \\ H \quad H \end{array}$$ (2)

**(c)** Alkenes are unsaturated because there is a carbon-carbon **(1)** double bond **(1)**

**(d)** $2C_3H_{6(g)} + 9O_{2(g)} \longrightarrow 6CO_{2(g)} + 6H_2O_{(l)}$ or $C_3H_{6(g)} + 4\frac{1}{2}O_{2(g)} \longrightarrow 3CO_{2(g)} + 3H_2O_{(l)}$ **(1 for formula of reactants and products, 1 for correctly balanced equation; ignore state symbols)**

**(e)**

$$\begin{array}{c} \quad H \quad H \quad H \\ \quad | \quad\; | \quad\; | \\ H-C-C-C-H \\ \quad | \quad\; | \quad\; | \\ \quad H \quad H \quad H \end{array}$$ (2)

**2. (a) Accept one from:** silica, alumina, porcelain **(1)**

**(b)** $C_4H_{10}$ **(1)**

**Page 30**

**1. (a)** R–OH **(allow –OH or OH) (1)**

**(b)** $CH_3CH_2OH$ **(1)**

**(c) Accept two from:** dissolve in water to form neutral solutions; react with sodium to produce hydrogen; burn in air to produce carbon dioxide and water **(2)**

**(d)** **Accept two from:** as fuels; as solvents; ethanol is the alcohol in alcoholic drinks **(2)**

**(e)**

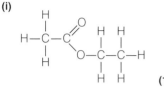 **(1)**

**(f)** **Accept two from:** dissolve in water to form acidic solutions; react with carbonates to form carbon dioxide; are weak acids i.e. they do not completely ionise when dissolved in water; react with alcohols in the presence of an acid catalyst to produce esters **(2)**

**(g)** It can be oxidised by heating with acidified potassium manganate(VII)/permanganate **(1)**

**(h)** Ethyl ethanoate **(1)**

**(i)**

**(1)**

## Page 31

1. **(a)** Ethene **(1)**

   **(b)**

   **(1)**

   **(c)** Addition polymer **(1)**

   **(d)** The carbon–carbon double bond **(1)**

   **(e)** Plastic shopping bags/carrier bags **(1)** water bottles **(1)** strong and light/easily moulded into shape **(1)**

2. **(a)** A polymer formed when molecule containing two functional groups react/join together **(1)** while eliminating a small molecule such as water **(1)**

   **(b)** A carboxylic acid group **(1)** and an amine group **(allow –COOH and –NH$_2$/COOH and NH$_2$) (1)**

   **(c)** Glucose **(1)**

## Page 32

1. **(a)** A mixture that has been designed as a useful product **(1)**

   **(b)** No **(1)** something that is chemically pure contains a single element or compound **(1)**

   **(c)** **Accept one from:** fuels; medicines; foods; fertilisers **(1)**

2. **(a)** The liquid solvent **(1 allow water)**

   **(b)** red and green **(1)** The spots of these colours are at the same height as spots in ink X **(1)**

   **(c)** $\frac{0.5}{4.65}$ = 0.11 **(allow 0.10–0.12; 1 mark for working, 1 mark for correct answer)**

   **(d)** It is more accurate/relative amounts of different inks can be determined/smaller quantities can be used **(1)**

## Page 33

1. **(a)** Calcium hydroxide **(1)**

   **(b)** A precipitate **(1)** of CaCO$_3$ **(1)** is formed

2. **(a)** The litmus paper turns red **(1)** before turning white/being bleached **(1)**

   **(b)** Acidic gas **(1)** as it turns litmus paper red **(1)**

3. **(a)** Hydrogen gives a squeaky pop **(1)** when exposed to a lit splint **(1)**

   **(b)** Oxygen relights **(1)** a glowing splint **(1)**

   **(c)** $2H_{2(g)} + O_{2(g)} \longrightarrow 2H_2O_{(l)}$ **(1 for formulae of reactants/ products, 1 for correctly balanced equation; ignore state symbols)**

## Page 34

1. Cu$^{2+}$ – blue/green **(1)** Li$^+$ – crimson red **(1)** Ca$^{2+}$ – brick red **(1)** Na$^+$ – yellow **(1)**

2. **(a)** A reaction in which a solid is produced **(1)** when two solutions react **(1)**

   **(b)** A blue precipitate **(1)**

**(c)** $Cu^{2+}_{(aq)} + 2OH^-_{(aq)} \longrightarrow Cu(OH)_{2(s)}$ **(1 for balanced equation/ correct formulae, 1 for correct state symbols)**

**(d)** Upon adding excess sodium hydroxide solution **(1)** the aluminium hydroxide precipitate will dissolve while the magnesium hydroxide precipitate remains **(1)**

**(e)** Fe$^{2+}$ gives a green precipitate with sodium hydroxide solution **(1)** Fe$^{3+}$ gives a brown precipitate with sodium hydroxide solution **(1)**

**(f)** Sodium hydroxide solution is added to the solution containing ammonium ions **(1)** this is then warmed and the vapour arising tested with moist red litmus paper **(1)**, which will turn blue **(1)**

## Page 35

1. **(a)** White **(1)**

   **(b)** Barium sulfate **(1)** BaSO$_4$ **(1)**

   **(c)** CO$_3$$^{2-}$ **(2)**

   **(d)** Add dilute (hydrochloric) acid **(1)** test the gas evolved by bubbling it through limewater **(1)**, which will turn milky/cloudy **(1)** in the presence of carbon dioxide gas

2. **(a)** Each halide ion forms a different coloured **(1)** precipitate **(1)** e.g. chloride ions form a white precipitate, bromide ions form a cream/off-white precipitate and iodide ions form a yellow precipitate

   **(b)** $Ag^+_{(aq)} + Cl^-_{(aq)} \longrightarrow AgCl_{(s)}$ **(1 for balanced equation, 1 for correct state symbols)**

3. **(a)** Flame emission spectrometer/flame photometer **(1)**

   **(b)** **Accept two from:** more accurate; more sensitive; can be used with very small sample sizes **(2)**

## Page 36

1. **(a)** Nitrogen or oxygen **(1)**

   **(b)** The water vapour originally in the atmosphere cooled **(1)** and condensed **(1)** forming the oceans

   **(c)** Green plants/algae **(1)** form oxygen as a waste product of photosynthesis **(1)**

   **(d)** **Accept two from:** green plants; algae use carbon dioxide for photosynthesis; carbon dioxide is used to form sedimentary rocks; carbon dioxide is captured in oil; coal **(2)**

## Page 37

1. **(a)** Greenhouse gases allow short wavelength radiation from the Sun to pass through the atmosphere **(1)** but absorb long wavelength radiation reflected back from the earth trapping heat **(1)**

   **(b)** **Accept one from:** methane; water vapour **(1)**

   **(c)** **Accept two from:** combustion of fossil fuels; deforestation; increased animal farming; decomposing rubbish in landfill sites **(2)**

   **(d)** There are many different factors contributing to climate change **(1)** and it is not easy to predict the impact of each one **(1)**

   **(e)** **Accept two from:** rising sea levels, which may cause flooding and coastal erosion; more frequent and/or severe storms; changes to the amount, timing and distribution of rainfall; temperature and water stress for humans and wildlife; changes to the food-producing capacity of some regions/changes to the distribution of wildlife species **(2)**

   **(f)** **Accept two from:** use of alternative energy supplies; increased use of renewable energy; energy conservation; carbon capture and storage techniques; carbon taxes and licences; carbon offsetting/carbon neutrality **(2)**

   **(g)** **Accept two from:** disagreement over the causes and consequences of global climate change; lack of public information and education; lifestyle changes, e.g. greater use of cars and aeroplanes; economic considerations, i.e. the financial costs of reducing the carbon footprint; incomplete international co-operation **(2)**

**Page 38**

1. (a) Fuel formed in the ground over millions of years from the remains of dead plants and animals **(1)**

   (b) Due to incomplete combustion/burning of fuels in a poor supply of oxygen **(1)**

   (c) **Accept one from:** forms acid rain; can cause respiratory problems **(1)**

   (d) Global dimming **(1)** health problems due to lung damage **(1)**

   (e) It combines with haemoglobin/red blood cells **(1)** preventing the transport of oxygen **(1)**

   (f) When sulfur burns it react with oxygen to form sulfur dioxide **(1)** Sulfur dioxide dissolves in rain water **(1)** The rain water is now acidic/acid rain which can damage buildings and destroy wildlife **(1)**

**Page 39**

1. (a) The needs of the current generation are met without compromising the potential of future generations to meet their own needs **(1)** Improving agricultural practices/using chemical processes to make new materials **(1)**

   (b) Water that is safe to drink **(1)**

   (c) Filtration/passed through filter beds to remove solid impurities **(1)** sterilised to kill microbes **(1)**

   (d) **Accept three from:** screening and grit removal; sedimentation to produce sewage sludge and effluent; anaerobic digestion of sewage sludge; aerobic biological treatment of effluent **(3)**

2. (a)

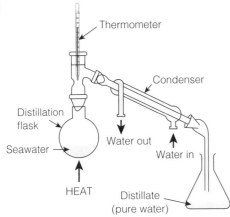

Thermometer

Condenser

Distillation flask

Seawater

Water out

Water in

HEAT

Distillate (pure water)

   **(3 for labelled diagram: seawater in flask, condenser, pure water being collected)**
   The water from the seawater boils/evaporates at 100°C and is condensed back into water in the condenser **(1)** the salt remains behind in the original flask **(1)**

   (b) Reverse osmosis **(1)**

**Page 40**

1. (a) A naturally occurring mineral **(1)** from which it is economically viable to extract a metal **(1)**

   (b) We still require the raw materials **(1)** but it is becoming increasingly difficult/uneconomic to mine them in traditional ways **(1)**

   (c) Electrical wiring **(1)** as it is a good conductor of electricity **(1)** water pipes **(1)** as it does not react with water/corrode **(1)**

   (d) Plants grow in a medium that enables them to absorb metal compounds **(1)** the plants are then harvested/burned leaving ash that is rich in the metal compounds **(1)** the ash is then further treated to extract the metal **(1)**

   (e) Bacteria extract metals from low-grade ores producing a solution rich in metal compounds **(1)**

   (f) iron + copper sulfate → iron sulfate + copper **(1 for reactants, 1 for products)**

   (g) Platinum is less reactive than copper/too low in reactivity/in the reactivity series **(1)** and so is unable to displace copper from copper compounds

   (h) Electrolysis **(1)**

**Page 41**

1. (a) **Accept two from:** extracting and processing raw materials; manufacturing and packaging; disposal at end of useful life **(2)**

   (b) **Accept two from:** how much energy is needed; how much water is used; what resources are required; how much waste is produced; how much pollution is produced **(2)**

   (c) Allocating numerical values to pollutant effects is not always easy or straightforward **(1)** so value judgments have to be made which may not always be objective **(1)**

   (d) To support claims for advertising purposes **(1)**

2. Over the life of the product, plastic bags when compared with paper bags (**accept two from the following**): use less energy; use less fossil fuel; produce fewer $CO_2$ emissions; produce less waste; use less freshwater **(2)** meaning that plastic/polythene bags are less damaging to the environment/have less of an environmental impact **(1)** than paper bags (**Allow reverse argument**)

**Page 42**

1. (a) Oxygen **(1)** and water **(1)**

   (b) Salt from the sea **(1)** speeds up/increases the rate **(1)** of rusting

   (c) The water was boiled to remove air/oxygen **(1)**; the oil prevented oxygen from entering **(1)**

   (d) **Accept two from:** greasing; painting; galvanising **(2)**

   (e) Nickel/chromium **(1)**

   (f) An alloy **(1)**

**Page 43**

1. (a) Nitrogen from (fractional distillation of liquid) air **(1)** hydrogen from natural gas **(1)**

   (b) Iron/Fe **(1)**

   (c) (i) Answer between 15% and 25% **(1)**

       (ii) As temperature increases, the yield of ammonia decreases **(1)**

   (d) 450°C **(1)**, 200 atms pressure **(1)**

   (e) Rate is too slow **(1)**, so ammonia will not be produced economically **(1)**

| Question number | | Answer | Notes | Marks |
|---|---|---|---|---|
| 1 | (a) | Each row begins with elements with one outer electron. | | 1 |
| | (b) | Their boiling points increase as you go down the group. | | 1 |
| | (c) | | Give 1 mark for an X anywhere in the grey area. | 1 |
| 2 | (a) | They make an alkali when reacted with water. | | 1 |
| | (b) | The outer electron in sodium is further from the nucleus. | | 1 |
| | | Less energy needed to remove the outer electron / the outer electron is less tightly held / less attractive force from nucleus to outer electron. | | 1 |
| 3 | (a) | lithium, calcium, zinc, iron | | 1 |
| | (b) | Form coloured compounds | | 1 |
| | (c) | Any two from: Steel is harder than iron. Steel is stronger than iron. Steel is less likely to corrode / rust than iron. | The answer must be a comparison. | 2 |
| | (d) | (Metal) ion / cation Electron → Electrons are delocalised / 'sea of electrons' Free to move | Give 1 mark for the (metal) ion / cation label and 1 mark for the electron label. | 1 / 1 / 1 / 1 |
| 4 | (a) | High melting point and slippery | | 1 |
| | (b) | $2.9 \times 10^7 \text{ cm}^2$ | This is how the answer is calculated: volume = area × height (thickness) $1 = \text{area} \times 3.4 \times 10^{-8}$ $\text{area} = \dfrac{1}{3.4 \times 10^{-8}}$ $= 2.9 \times 10^7 \text{ cm}^2$ | 1 |
| | (c) | Any two from: high (tensile) strength high electrical conductivity high thermal conductivity. | | 2 |
| | (d) | High melting point because of: giant structure / lots of bonds / macromolecule strong bonds / lots of energy to break bonds. Does not conduct electricity because: there are no free / mobile electrons **or** all its electrons are used in bonding. | | 1 / 1 / 1 |
| 5 | (a) | copper(II) carbonate → copper(II) oxide + carbon dioxide | | 1 |
| | (b) | 12.35 – 7.95 = | | 1 |
| | | 4.40 (g) | Accept 4.4 (g) | 1 |
| 6 | (a) | | Accept – / e / x as electrons. | 1 |

| Question number | Answer | Notes | Marks |
|---|---|---|---|
| **(b) (i)** | [2]Mg + O$_2$ → [2]MgO | | 1 |
| **(ii)** | There is only one product / all atoms end up in the product. | | 1 |
| **(iii)** | Accept either of the diagrams below:<br><br>Mg$^{2+}$  :O: $^{2-}$    :Mg:  :O: $^{2+}$ $^{2-}$ | Allow either dots for magnesium's electrons and crosses for oxygen's electrons<br>**or**<br>crosses for magnesium's electrons and dots for oxygen's electrons. | |
| | | Give 1 mark for both correct structures. | 1 |
| | | Give 1 mark for both charges correct. | 1 |
| **(c)** | % yield = $\dfrac{\text{mass product actually made}}{\text{maximum theoretical mass of product}} \times 100$<br><br>**or**  $\dfrac{9.6}{12.8} \times 100$<br><br>= 75% | | 1<br><br>1 |
| **7 (a)** | It has the same number of electrons and protons. | | 1 |
| **(b) (i)** | | Number of protons in the particle | **26** |<br>| Number of neutrons in the particle | **28** |<br>| Number of electrons in the particle | **24** | | Only award 1 mark if all three numbers are correct. | 1 |
| **(ii)** | **Protons:** the atomic number / number on the bottom left of symbol<br>**Neutrons:** 54 – 26 = 28 / mass number – atomic number<br>**Electrons:** 26 – 2 = 24 / atomic number but 2 electrons have been removed to make 2+ | | 1<br>1<br><br>1 |
| **8** | **Similarities:**<br>They have the same number of protons / atomic number.<br>They have the same number of electrons.<br>**Difference:**<br>Different number of neutrons / mass number. | | 1<br>1<br><br>1 |
| **9** | $\dfrac{1.2 \times 10^{-6}}{1.5 \times 10^{-10}}$<br><br>8000 or 8.0 × 10$^3$ | Allow 1 mark for working, even if the answer is not correct. | 1<br><br>1 |
| **10 (a)** | Copper oxide and sulfuric acid | | 1 |
| **(b)** | The pH would start high and decrease to below 7. | | 1 |
| **(c)** | Nitric acid | | 1 |
| **(d) (i)** | M$_r$ CaO = 56 **and** M$_r$ CaCl$_2$ = 111<br><br>5.55 g = $\dfrac{1}{20}$ mole or 0.05 mole CaO<br><br>Reaction ratio: 1:1<br><br>$\dfrac{1}{20}$ × 56 or 0.05 × 56 = 2.8 g | | 1<br><br>1<br>1<br>1 |
| **(ii)** | 69%<br><br>$\dfrac{138}{200} \times 100$ | Allow 2 marks for working, even if the answer is not correct:<br><br>Total product = 138<br>Total reactant = 200 | 1<br><br>1<br>1 |

| Question number | Answer | Notes | Marks |
|---|---|---|---|
| 11 (a) | The breakdown / decomposition of a substance | | 1 |
| | using an electric current. | Also accept: using electricity. | 1 |
| (b) | Cathode reaction is reduction because of<br>gain of electrons **or**<br>decrease in oxidation number. | | 1 |
| | Anode reaction is oxidation because of<br>loss of electrons **or**<br>increase in oxidation number. | | 1 |
| 12 (a) | $Fe_2O_3 + 3CO \rightarrow 2Fe + 3CO_2$ | Allow 1 mark for:<br>$Fe_2O_3 + CO \rightarrow Fe + CO_2$ | 2 |
| (b) | Copper is less reactive than carbon / copper is lower in the reactivity series than carbon / or reverse argument (ora). | | 1 |
| | Aluminium is more reactive than carbon / aluminium is higher in the reactivity series than carbon / ora. | | 1 |
| (c) | **Cathode:** $Al^{3+} + 3e^- \rightarrow Al$ | | 1 |
| | **Anode:** $2O^{2-} \rightarrow O_2 + 4e^-$ | | 1 |
| 13 (a) | Any two from:<br>They don't run out (provided there is a supply of fuel).<br>They do not have to be recharged.<br>The only product is water / there is no pollution. | | 2 |
| (b) (i) | $H_2 \rightarrow 2H^+ + 2e^-$ | Accept 2e. | 1 |
| (ii) | $O_2 + 4e^- \rightarrow 2O^{2-}$ | Accept 4e. | 1 |
| (c) | The product line ($2H_2O$) needs to be below the reactant line. | | 1 |
| | $2H_2O$ should be on the product line. | | 1 |
| | Activation energy should be labelled correctly (the arrows must touch or almost touch the lines). | | 1 |

14 (a)

| Solid | Start temperature (°C) | End temperature (°C) | Temperature change (°C) | | |
|---|---|---|---|---|---|
| Ammonium chloride | 15 | 9 | −6 | Award 1 mark for two correct numbers and 1 mark for two correct signs. | 2 |
| Potassium hydroxide | 16 | 29 | +13 | | |
| Ammonium nitrate | 18 | 4 | **−14** | | |
| Sodium hydroxide | 17 | 35 | **+18** | | |

| Question number | Answer | Notes | Marks |
|---|---|---|---|
| (b) | Ammonium nitrate | | 1 |
| | Endothermic reactions cause the temperature to decrease. | | 1 |
| | Ammonium nitrate had the biggest drop in temperature. | | 1 |
| 15 (a) | **Arrangement** – any one from:<br>Molecules move further apart.<br>Molecules are less ordered / more random. | | 1 |
| | **Movement** – any one from:<br>Molecules gain kinetic energy.<br>Molecules move faster.<br>Molecules move more randomly. | | 1 |
| (b) | 15 000 g of oxygen $= \dfrac{15\,000}{32} = 468.75$ moles | | 1 |
| | Volume $= 468.75$ moles $\times 24 = 11\,250$ dm$^3$ | | 1 |

| Question number | Answer | Notes | Marks |
|---|---|---|---|
| 16 | Level 3: Correct descriptions of the development of at least three atomic models and the linking of two scientists. | | 5–6 |
| | Level 2: Correct descriptions of the development of at least two atomic models and the linking of one scientist. | | 3–4 |
| | Level 1: One correct description of the development of any atomic model. | | 1–2 |
| | No relevant content | | 0 |
| | **Indicative content** | | |
| | 'Plum pudding' model of the atom / existence of electrons – J.J. Thomson<br>Nuclear model / 'solar system' atom – Marsden and Rutherford<br>Electron orbits – Niels Bohr<br>Existence of neutrons – James Chadwick | | |
| 17 (a) | First test – the iodide converted (oxidised) to iodine.<br>Bromine is more reactive than iodine.<br>No reaction in second test<br>because bromine is less reactive than chlorine. | | 1<br>1<br>1<br>1 |
| (b) | <br>or<br> | Give 1 mark for the shared pair of electrons.<br><br>Give 1 mark if the rest of the diagram is correct. | 1<br><br>1 |
| (c) | Chlorine has weaker forces between molecules / weaker intermolecular forces.<br>Less energy is needed to separate molecules in chlorine. | Allow 'stronger' forces for iodine.<br><br>Allow 'more energy' for iodine. | 1<br>1 |
| (d) | It has no free electrons / the electrons cannot move / all outer electrons are involved in bonding. | | 1 |
| 18 (a) | $\dfrac{14.4}{12} = 1.2$ mole<br>$1.2 \times 393 = 472$ kJ | Accept 471.6 kJ | 1<br>1 |
| (b) | Energy is taken in to break (oxygen) bonds.<br>Energy is given out, making (C=O) bonds.<br>More energy is given out than taken in. | | 1<br>1<br>1 |
| (c) | Any three from:<br>• Use a more accurate method of measuring the volumes, e.g. a 25 cm$^3$ pipette or a 25 cm$^3$ measuring cylinder.<br>• Use an insulated beaker / polystyrene cup.<br>• Use separate apparatus to measure the acid.<br>• Measure the start temperature before adding the acid.<br>• Wait until there is no further temperature change before measuring the final temperature.<br>• Repeat the method at least two more times. | | 3 |

| Question number | | Answer | Notes | Marks |
|---|---|---|---|---|
| 1 | (a) | Chlorine | | 1 |
| | (b) | Methane | | 1 |
| | (c) | Carbon dioxide | | 1 |
| 2 | (a) | Breaking up / decomposing (large molecules) | | 1 |
| | | into smaller / more useful substances / molecules. | | 1 |
| | (b) | Any one from: They act as a catalyst. They speed up the reaction. They provide a surface on which the reaction happens. | | 1 |
| | (c) | $C_{16}H_{34} \rightarrow C_{10}H_{22} + 3C_2H_4$ | If balancing is not correct, allow 1 mark for: $C_{16}H_{34} \rightarrow C_{10}H_{22} + C_2H_4$ | 2 |
| 3 | | Any three from: Small molecules have weaker (intermolecular) forces / large molecules have stronger forces. Small molecules have lower boiling point / large molecules have higher boiling point. Stronger forces lead to a higher boiling point / weaker forces lead to a lower boiling point. Fractions are separated by different boiling points. | | 3 |
| 4 | | $C_5H_{12}$ | | 1 |
| 5 | (a) | Dylan | | 1 |
| | (b) | The acid was the limiting reagent in her experiment / all of the acid had been used up in her experiment. | Allow: magnesium in excess. | 1 |
| | | Magnesium was the limiting reagent in the other experiments / all of the magnesium was used up in the other experiments. | Allow: acid in excess. | 1 |
| | (c) (i) | mean rate = $\dfrac{\text{quantity of product formed}}{\text{time taken}} = \dfrac{94.5}{225} =$ | | 1 |
| | | 0.42 | | 1 |
| | | Unit = $cm^3/s$ | | 1 |
| | (ii) | The volume of gas will double | | 1 |
| | | because the volume of gas is dependent on the amount of magnesium. | | 1 |
| 6 | (a) | C and D | | 1 |
| | (b) | $0.86 = \dfrac{\text{distance moved by B}}{7.91} = 0.86 \times 7.91$ | | 1 |
| | | = 6.80 | 6.8 / 6.802 / 6.8026 is worth 1 mark. | 1 |
| 7 | | Ammonium phosphate and potassium chloride | | 1 |
| 8 | (a) | | | 1 |
| | (b) | $2C_4H_{10} + 13O_2 \rightarrow 8CO_2 + 10H_2O$ | If balancing is not correct, allow 1 mark for: $C_4H_{10} + O_2 \rightarrow CO_2 + H_2O$ If all the numbers are correct, allow multiples for balancing. | 2 |
| 9 | (a) | Any two from: yeast absence of air in aqueous solution / dissolved in water. | | 2 |

| Question number | Answer | Notes | Marks |
|---|---|---|---|
| **(b)** | The reaction stops because <br> yeast is killed / enzymes in yeast are denatured. | Do not accept: the enzymes are killed. | 1 <br> 1 |
| **(c)** | **Advantage** – any one from: <br> it is renewable <br> flammable <br> burns with a clean flame / no incomplete combustion <br> fermentation does not need high temperatures. <br><br> **Disadvantage** – any one from: <br> it has to be purified / purification is expensive <br> reaction has low yield <br> carbon dioxide is made by the reaction; it is a greenhouse gas <br> land used to grow sugar crops rather than food crops. | | 1 <br><br><br><br><br> 1 |
| **(d)** | Ethyl ethanoate | | 1 |
| **10** | Composite | | 1 |
| **11** | 1.69 g | Pure gold = 24 carats, 9 carats = $\frac{9}{24}$th gold <br> $\frac{9}{24} \times 4.5 = 1.69$ (rounded up) | 1 |
| **12 (a)** | D, A, C, B | Allow 1 mark if D and A are in the correct order. | 2 |
| **(b)** | It is a simple or complex explanation put forward by scientists <br><br> to try and explain observations/facts | | 1 <br><br> 1 |
| **(c)** | It cannot be proved because it was so long ago / there is insufficient evidence to confirm the theory. | | 1 |
| **(d)** | | | 1 |
| **13 (a)** | <br> All six points correctly plotted <br> Smooth curve | Allow 1 mark for four or five points correctly plotted; 1 mark deducted if the graph is plotted dot to dot rather than as a smooth curve. | 2 <br> 1 |

| Question number | Answer | Notes | Marks |
|---|---|---|---|
| (b) | Rate increases as concentration increases. | | 1 |
| | Increased concentration means more crowded particles / more particles in same space / volume. | | 1 |
| | More chance of collision / more frequent collisions. | | 1 |
| (c) | The reaction times would be smaller / shorter / less. | | 1 |
| 14 | **Desalination:** removal of salt from the water / changing sea water into drinking water. | | 1 |
| | **Chlorination:** adding chlorine to kill bacteria / germs / microorganisms. | | 1 |
| 15 (a) | Level 3: Correct explanation of each of the four tests and a full description of a flame test. Confirms the presence of sulfate but not copper(II) ions. | | 5–6 |
| | Level 2: Correct explanation of two of the four tests **and** a full description of a flame test. | | 3–4 |
| | Level 1: Correct explanation of two of the four tests **or** a full description of a flame test. | | 1–2 |
| | No relevant content | | 0 |
| | **Indicative content** | | |
| | **Flame test** | | |
| | Use a flame test wire / spray sample through the flame. Dip wire into solution. Put wire or substance into a (blue) Bunsen flame. Observe the colour of the flame. | A full description includes at least three of these points. | |
| | **Tests** | | |
| | The flame test indicates lithium ions in the water. Silver nitrate indicates bromide ions in the water. Barium chloride indicates sulfate ions in the water. Sodium hydroxide indicates iron(III) ions in the water. | | |
| | The results support the idea that the river water contains sulfate ions but not copper(II) ions. | | |
| (b) | It would show if other metal ions are present. | | 1 |
| | It would measure the concentration of the metal ions. | | 1 |
| 16 (a) | 50% | | 1 |
| (b) | The yield decreases. | | 1 |
| (c) | If pressure increases, the reaction goes in the direction that reduces the number of moles of gas / the volume of gases, i.e. the direction with the fewest number of moles of gas. | | 1 |
| | The equilibrium moves to the right / forward direction / to the product side. | | 1 |
| (d) | High pressures need energy / equipment that can tolerate high pressures, and this is expensive. | | 1 |
| | The costs outweigh the benefits of a higher yield. | | 1 |
| 17 (a) | B | | 1 |
| | Powder reacts faster / line steeper on graph | | 1 |
| | because powder has a larger surface area. | | 1 |
| | More chance of successful collisions / more frequent successful collisions. | | 1 |
| (b) | | The curve must start at reactants, be lower than the original curve and end at products. | 1 |

| Question number | Answer | Notes | Marks |
|---|---|---|---|
| 18 | Alloys are harder.<br>Alloys have a lower density.<br>Alloys have a lower melting point.<br>Alloys are stronger. | Allow the reverse argument, e.g. pure metals are softer. | 4 |
| 19 | Any two from:<br>Zinc provides a barrier (to water and air).<br>Zinc is more reactive than iron / steel.<br>Zinc loses electrons more readily than iron / steel.<br>Zinc reacts instead of iron / steel. | Accept: Zinc reacts first / Zinc reacts before the iron … | 2 |
| 20 (a) | \n\nAccept curved or square brackets. | Award 1 mark for side links;<br>1 mark for $n$; I mark for the rest of the molecule (must have only one $CH_3$ group). | 3 |
| (b) (i) | Forces between the molecules are overcome.<br><br>Polymer chains can move past each other (they become soft). | | 1<br><br>1 |
| (ii) | The forces between the chains are too strong.<br><br>It has cross-links / covalent bonds between the chains. | | 1<br><br>1 |
| (iii) | They were made under different reaction conditions.<br><br>They were made with a different catalyst. | | 1<br><br>1 |
| 21 (a) | As the reaction progresses, the rate of the backward reaction increases until the rates of the forward and backward reactions are the same. | | 1<br>1 |
| (b) | Favours the reverse reaction / equilibrium position moves to the left / moves to the reactant side.<br><br>Reaction goes in the direction to increase the number of moles / reactants have a larger volume / reaction works to increase pressure on the side with higher moles of gas. | | 1<br><br><br>1 |
| (c) | No effect on the equilibrium position. | | 1 |
| (d) | Which reaction direction is exothermic / which reaction direction is endothermic. | | 1 |
| 22 (a) | Alcohol / –OH<br><br>Carboxylic acid / –COOH | Allow acyl chloride. | 1<br><br>1 |
| (b) | Water is also made / a small molecule is also made. | | 1 |
| (c) | Difficult to know how far a product or waste will travel. | | 1 |
| 23 (a) | Nitrogen **and** oxygen from the air<br>react in the high temperatures<br>in the engine. | | 1<br>1<br>1 |
| (b) (i) | One from: causes acid rain / causes respiratory problems. | | 1 |
| (ii) | Remove sulfur from the fuel before use. | | 1 |

# Notes

# Notes

# Periodic Table

**Key**

◼ Metals
◻ Non-metals

| | | | | | | | | | 0 or 8 |
|---|---|---|---|---|---|---|---|---|---|
| | | | **3** | **4** | **5** | **6** | **7** | | 4<br>**He**<br>helium<br>2 |
| **1** | **2** | | 7<br>**Li**<br>lithium<br>3 | | | | | | |

Key box:
Relative atomic mass → 1
Atomic symbol → **H**
Name → hydrogen
Atomic number → 1

| Group 1 | Group 2 | | | | | | | | | | | | | Group 3 | Group 4 | Group 5 | Group 6 | Group 7 | Group 0 or 8 |
|---|---|---|---|---|---|---|---|---|---|---|---|---|---|---|---|---|---|---|---|
| | | | | | | | | | | | | | | | | | | | 4<br>**He**<br>helium<br>2 |
| 7<br>**Li**<br>lithium<br>3 | 9<br>**Be**<br>beryllium<br>4 | | | | | | | | | | | | | 11<br>**B**<br>boron<br>5 | 12<br>**C**<br>carbon<br>6 | 14<br>**N**<br>nitrogen<br>7 | 16<br>**O**<br>oxygen<br>8 | 19<br>**F**<br>fluorine<br>9 | 20<br>**Ne**<br>neon<br>10 |
| 23<br>**Na**<br>sodium<br>11 | 24<br>**Mg**<br>magnesium<br>12 | | | | | | | | | | | | | 27<br>**Al**<br>aluminium<br>13 | 28<br>**Si**<br>silicon<br>14 | 31<br>**P**<br>phosphorus<br>15 | 32<br>**S**<br>sulfur<br>16 | 35.5<br>**Cl**<br>chlorine<br>17 | 40<br>**Ar**<br>argon<br>18 |
| 39<br>**K**<br>potassium<br>19 | 40<br>**Ca**<br>calcium<br>20 | 45<br>**Sc**<br>scandium<br>21 | 48<br>**Ti**<br>titanium<br>22 | 51<br>**V**<br>vanadium<br>23 | 52<br>**Cr**<br>chromium<br>24 | 55<br>**Mn**<br>manganese<br>25 | 56<br>**Fe**<br>iron<br>26 | 59<br>**Co**<br>cobalt<br>27 | 59<br>**Ni**<br>nickel<br>28 | 63.5<br>**Cu**<br>copper<br>29 | 65<br>**Zn**<br>zinc<br>30 | | | 70<br>**Ga**<br>gallium<br>31 | 73<br>**Ge**<br>germanium<br>32 | 75<br>**As**<br>arsenic<br>33 | 79<br>**Se**<br>selenium<br>34 | 80<br>**Br**<br>bromine<br>35 | 84<br>**Kr**<br>krypton<br>36 |
| 85<br>**Rb**<br>rubidium<br>37 | 88<br>**Sr**<br>strontium<br>38 | 89<br>**Y**<br>yttrium<br>39 | 91<br>**Zr**<br>zirconium<br>40 | 93<br>**Nb**<br>niobium<br>41 | 96<br>**Mo**<br>molybdenum<br>42 | [98]<br>**Tc**<br>technetium<br>43 | 101<br>**Ru**<br>ruthenium<br>44 | 103<br>**Rh**<br>rhodium<br>45 | 106<br>**Pd**<br>palladium<br>46 | 108<br>**Ag**<br>silver<br>47 | 112<br>**Cd**<br>cadmium<br>48 | | | 115<br>**In**<br>indium<br>49 | 119<br>**Sn**<br>tin<br>50 | 122<br>**Sb**<br>antimony<br>51 | 128<br>**Te**<br>tellurium<br>52 | 127<br>**I**<br>iodine<br>53 | 131<br>**Xe**<br>xenon<br>54 |
| 133<br>**Cs**<br>caesium<br>55 | 137<br>**Ba**<br>barium<br>56 | 139<br>**La***<br>lanthanum<br>57 | 178<br>**Hf**<br>hafnium<br>72 | 181<br>**Ta**<br>tantalum<br>73 | 184<br>**W**<br>tungsten<br>74 | 186<br>**Re**<br>rhenium<br>75 | 190<br>**Os**<br>osmium<br>76 | 192<br>**Ir**<br>iridium<br>77 | 195<br>**Pt**<br>platinum<br>78 | 197<br>**Au**<br>gold<br>79 | 201<br>**Hg**<br>mercury<br>80 | | | 204<br>**Tl**<br>thallium<br>81 | 207<br>**Pb**<br>lead<br>82 | 209<br>**Bi**<br>bismuth<br>83 | [209]<br>**Po**<br>polonium<br>84 | [210]<br>**At**<br>astatine<br>85 | [222]<br>**Rn**<br>radon<br>86 |
| [223]<br>**Fr**<br>francium<br>87 | [226]<br>**Ra**<br>radium<br>88 | [227]<br>**Ac***<br>actinium<br>89 | [261]<br>**Rf**<br>rutherfordium<br>104 | [262]<br>**Db**<br>dubnium<br>105 | [266]<br>**Sg**<br>seaborgium<br>106 | [264]<br>**Bh**<br>bohrium<br>107 | [277]<br>**Hs**<br>hassium<br>108 | [268]<br>**Mt**<br>meitnerium<br>109 | [271]<br>**Ds**<br>darmstadtium<br>110 | [272]<br>**Rg**<br>roentgenium<br>111 | | | | | | | | | |